N.P.1840
THE LOSS OF THE
"ATLANTIC CONVEYOR"

BY
CHARLES DROUGHT

To Bill

Best Regards

First Published 2003 by Countyvise Limited, 14 Appin Road, Birkenhead, Wirral CH41 9HH in conjunction with the author Charles Drought

Copyright © 2003 Charles Drought

The right of Charles Drought to be identified as the author of this work has been asserted by him in accordance with the Copyright, Design and Patents Act 1988.

British Library Cataloguing in Publication Data.
A catalogue record for this book is available from the British Library.

ISBN 1 901231 41 0

CHAPTERS

This book is dedicated to my dear late wife Betty and my two sons, Christopher and Gareth, who courageously endured all my trials and tribulations during the Falklands conflict.

ACKNOWLEDGMENTS

First and foremost in writing this acknowledgement I must express my deep sense of gratitude to Mr Derek A Clulow, a retired Port of Manchester Pilot who, at my request, gave up his much prized leisure time to research and transfer my experiences on that fateful voyage aboard the 'Atlantic Conveyor' to the Falklands conflict, into this book. Without his help and expertise my story could never have been told and I sincerely thank him for his patience and forbearance over the many months it took him to produce this book.

I am no less grateful to all the people and the establishments named below for their courtesy and assistance in allowing me to use the many photographs illustrated within these pages and the considerable information they made available. A special thank you to Mr. T Searle for his expertise in computer enhancement of some of the photographs contained in this book, his work was invaluable in writing this book. Mr. John Pugh, a columnist for the Liverpool Daily Post, whose advice and editing greatly enhanced the writing of this story, Mr. G. Ross, Chief Engineer, for his superb help in converting the text to a computerised disc, his work was so important in producing this book.

Finally to all the people and establishments who contributed, who I may have forgotten, my sincere thank you to you all.

Wright Logan, Portsmouth.
Ms. C. Neil, RFD Life Rafts, Belfast.
Mr. F. Schofield author "The Falklands Watcher".
Mr. N. Staples, Records Officer Maritime and Coastguard Agency.
Mr. J. Stewart, Chief Eng, "Atlantic Conveyor"
Mr. P. Bailey, 2nd Officer, "Atlantic Conveyor"
Mr. E. Jarvis, Steward, "Atlantic Conveyor"
Mrs. L. Stein
Mrs. G. Ross, Typist for the original manuscript
Mrs. J. Ross.

"Whatever is facing us, there is but one way to meet it - to go straight forward, to bear what has to be borne. Have faith that right makes might and in that faith let us to the end do our duty as we understand it."

ABRAHAM LINCOLN

Mr Charles Drought, Senior Third Engineer
'Atlantic Conveyor', May 1982

1

AT HOME

Spring had arrived early on the Wirral that year, and in the middle of April she was in all her glory and nothing was going to deter her from showing off her new array of colours. On that morning in 1982 a cloudless blue sky was a perfect background for a multitude of colours in Charles Drought's garden. The majestic magnolia tree was gowned in white flowers, the brilliant yellows of the daffodils contrasted with the blood reds of the tulips and the variegated polyanthus. The sward of fresh green grass of the lawn completed a picture that could have been painted by Monet. How true the sage's words "April prepares her green traffic light and the world thinks go."

A gentle southerly wind drifted over this masterpiece of nature, carrying with it the fresh smell of a spring morning through a half opened window, and gently billowed the curtains of a neat and orderly bedroom where Charles lay in a deep and undisturbed sleep between snow white sheets. The breeze caressed his rugged face as though urging him to awake and see this wonder of nature unfolding on a perfect spring day.

Charles stirred comfortably, then sighed contentedly. Very slowly he began to surface and stretched luxuriously, but a slight twinge of oncoming cramp in his leg hastily made him abandon this act. Still heavy from sleep he rubbed his eyes and yawned; no need for alarm clocks for Charles, for more years than he cared to remember he always awoke at 0730hrs every morning. He turned his head towards the open window, but he could only see the clear blue sky and a few wispy white vapour trails made by a high-flying jet. He lay savouring the luxury of a lie-in and the prospect of a day of doing absolutely nothing.

Charles Drought was a third engineer with the Cunard-Brocklebank line and had docked in Tilbury, London, on the container vessel ACT 2 after a five month voyage which had taken him to Australia, New Zealand, and Northern Europe, and he was now really enjoying his well-earned leave. He swung his long legs out of the bed and pushed his feet into soft slippers and pulled on a light dressing gown. He strolled over to the half opened window and flung it fully open and took a deep breath filling his lungs with the fresh morning air. His gaze swept over the multi-coloured garden; the neatness, symmetry and colours never failed to amaze him at any time of the year. He shook his head and said aloud to himself: "How the hell does she do it? She's a bloody marvel, that's for sure."

All the planning and organising of the garden was his wife's forte. Betty was a farmer's daughter and a self-taught brilliant horticulturist. Charles would occasionally help in the garden when on leave, if put under pressure by Betty, but he always referred to gardening, in his jokey little way, as "Woman's Work". It was not an unusual observation to come from a seafarer.

He turned away from the window and went into the bathroom and methodically performed his usual morning routine of ablutions, finishing up with a cold shower, a habit of a lifetime at sea. Dressing casually for a lazy day, he walked down the stairs, picked up the newspaper and a scattering of mail off the hall floor and walked into the kitchen.

"Morning love, great day, sleep well?" he asked.

"Once you stopped snoring I did," she sharply replied.

"Come off it Betty, I didn't snore," he said. She stared hard at him, hands on hip. Charles knew this stance only too well. "Don't push it son," he said to himself.

"Well, if I did I could not hear it so it could not have been that loud," he smiled.

"No, you wouldn't, you never do hear a thing. Once your head hits that pillow you are dead," Betty retorted. This deep sleep syndrome was in direct contrast to the 23 years he had been sea-going when he was the lightest of sleepers and would be awakened by the slightest noise.

Betty was not really angry or annoyed with Charles; she loved him deeply and missed him terribly when he was away at sea. Every moment was precious to her when Charles was on leave, and when he was away she constantly worried about his health and safety, but was always careful never to let these feelings show or speak of them. Charles leant heavily with his hands on the breakfast table. "What's it to be this morning then? The full monty - eggs, bacon, tomatoes, hash browns, or shall I make the snooker man's breakfast 'two blacks', black coffee and black toast?" he joked.

"Sorry Charles, not much time for breakfast this morning. Don't you remember Janet and Jack are coming over for lunch this afternoon, and we have a thousand and one things to do before they arrive," she replied.

"Where do you get the 'we' from?" placing great emphasis on the 'we'. "They are your cousins not mine, and anyway they are a nosy pair."

"Now then Charles," she gently rebuked him. "You know we always ask them over when you are on leave, it's the only time I get to see them and besides, they are really interested in hearing where you have been to on your last trip."

"You are right love, they think the Isle of Man is overseas and it will be nice for you to see them and have a good old chat together, catching up on family matters."

Betty made the coffee and toast and they sat down at the breakfast table.

"What are we going to give them for lunch?" Charles asked.

"Just a little salad. Janet's on one of her diet kicks again."

"That doesn't mean I have to go on a Dachau Diet so she can look like Twiggy, does it? With hardly any breakfast and a salad for lunch I will be starving by tonight."

Betty remained silent and Charles knew instinctively not to pursue this line of reasoning and immediately changed to another subject.

"More importantly, what shall we have for drinks?" he wanted to know.

"Just have one bottle of red wine and a bottle of white," Betty quickly replied.

"That's not enough for the four of us," said Charles ruefully.

"I don't know about that, you and Jack will probably drink most of it. Janet's diet bans alcohol, and I won't be having more than one glass because we are eating out tonight," she said hopefully, "and you know what that means - more drinks before, during and after the meal and you will be driving."

"So what, two bottles is still not enough."

"Oh isn't it? No doubt when we get home from the 'Coach' you will have the usual night-cap, and then you end up snoring like the Bar Light vessel fog horn all night and no sleep for me again," she complained. "It's two bottles of wine or nothing."

Charles knew he was beaten but he smiled lovingly across the table.

"Aye, I suppose you are right, as usual, two bottles it will be then."

Charles rose with a large theatrical sigh.

"Don't be feeling too hard done to, Charles Drought, you know damn well I am right," she admonished with a smile. Charles returned a rueful smile and helped to clear away the breakfast dishes. He kissed her lightly on the cheek and carried his second cup of coffee and the newspaper into the lounge.

The lounge was his favourite room, and the sun streaming through the patio windows gave the room a bright warm feeling and a sense of peacefulness to Charles that morning. He sat down in the chair from which he could see most of the garden, took a sip of his coffee and opened the newspaper to read all about the Falklands Crisis. It troubled him greatly, this Falklands affair. He lowered the paper on to his knees and stared unseeingly out of the patio window. The news had broken the serenity and peacefulness he had awakened with, and a strong sense of uneasiness came over him.

He shivered involuntary as if someone had walked over his grave. He was only too well aware of the state of the British Merchant Navy. It had been slowly eroded away over the years by a combination of greedy ship owners, foreign flag vessels and lack of subsidies from successive governments, until they had hardly any large cargo vessels left, or any ships at all for that matter. Deep in thought, and not very pleasant ones either, he was suddenly brought back to reality by the ringing of the telephone.

"I'll get it," he called out to Betty who was still working in the kitchen. He heaved himself out of his chair and walked into the hallway and picked up the jangling receiver, at the same time glancing at the clock. It was 10 o'clock.

"Morning, Charles Drought speaking."

"Ah good morning Mr Drought. Mr Pitter here, Cunard's Personnel Manager. How are you this morning," said a cheery voice.

Charles groaned inwardly, he knew only too well over many years of experience that any call from the personnel department when on leave could only mean one thing, to cut short your leave.

"OK until you rang," Charles gruffly replied.

"Sorry about that," Mr Pitter continued in a semi-jocular tone, "but it is vitally important. We have just heard that there is a possibility that the Ministry of Defence, in connection with the Falklands situation, could requisition the 'Atlantic Conveyor'." There was a pause. "Would you be prepared to go on a 48 hour notice to join her in Liverpool?"

Charles thought for a second. He knew his leave was coming to an end shortly and he always tried to be loyal to his employers - he had never ever refused to join any ship at any time - but this was an entirely different matter: a situation that could well be fraught with danger. True to form, Charles stood by his ideals of a lifetime, and after the slightest hesitation said, "Yes, I will go on standby for 48 hours Mr Pitter."

"Thank you Mr Drought. I will ring back as soon as I get any more news," and abruptly rang off before Charles could ask him any questions about what duty the 'Conveyor' was to be requisitioned for.

Charles stood for a minute holding the telephone in his hand, deep in thought. "How in the hell am I going to tell Betty of this development?" he said to himself. He gently replaced the receiver back and rubbed his chin with his hand, a habit he had formed over the years whenever he came against a tricky situation or problem. He knew it would be no good waffling around with some cock and bull story, Betty was too old a hand to be conned into some lame explanation. He took a deep breath and walked leaden footed towards the kitchen where he could hear Betty gaily singing away.

Betty had started making all the preparations for the forthcoming lunch.

"Who was that on the phone, dear?" she asked happily as he entered the kitchen.

"It was Mr Pitter from Cunard personnel ... " Before he could finish what he was going to tell her, Betty turned quickly around to face him. "What did he want? "she asked anxiously.

"It was Mr Pitter from Cunard personnel," he repeated. "I have been put on 48 hours notice to join the Atlantic Conveyor in Liverpool. It's something to do with the Ministry of Defence - they might requisition her for this Falklands foul up." He did not dare look Betty straight in the eyes.

Betty stood rooted to the spot, looking at him from across the kitchen table. In all her married life she always accepted, philosophically, Charles leaving to rejoin whichever vessel he had been appointed to, it was all part of being a seaman's wife. At this very moment, for the first time ever, she felt really frightened at the prospect of him going away. She had this strange premonition that something was going to happen to Charles. Betty stood there unable to say anything, just staring at him. Charles eventually met her gaze. "You are not worried are you? Now look here, the 'Conveyor' is a real strongly built ship with extra thick plating. I know this because, if you remember, I have sailed in her before," he said, trying to dispel any apprehensions she had. "Anyway, in all probability if she is requisitioned we will be only used to ferry supplies from the UK to the Ascension Islands in the South Atlantic. There is nothing really to get upset about at all."

Betty's intuition told her that there was more to it than just ferrying supplies. "I suppose you could be right," she said not very convincingly, and turned away to continue preparing lunch, but the dread of something happening to Charles persisted within her and it took all her strength to control her emotions.

The beautiful weather continued to bless them throughout the day. Janet and Jack duly arrived and they all sat out in the garden in the lovely warm spring sunshine. Charles had gone down to the local liquor store and picked up two bottles of wine as instructed, but as it happened Jack had been thoughtful enough to bring two bottles of wine as well. With all thoughts of abstemiousness banished by the 10 o'clock phone call from Cunard, Charles with Jack's help indulged in a good lunchtime session.

Betty remained strangely quiet, hardly talking about family affairs or anything, nor hardly touching the lunch she had prepared.

At about half-past three Janet and Jack bade their farewells, and Charles gave Betty a hand clearing away the lunch table and washing the dishes. By five o'clock that evening no further phone calls had been made from Cunard. Charles and Betty began to unwind a little, sitting in the garden swing savouring the last of a beautiful spring day.

"Maybe the MoD don't want the 'Conveyor' after all," Charles said hopefully.

"Don't hold your breath on that one."

"Listen Betty, lets get showered, put on our best 'go ashore' gear, and head out for dinner to the Coach and Horses at Moreton."

"Why not, it's not going to do us any good just sitting here all night brooding on what might or might not happen, let's go and get ready."

They were in the bedroom partly dressed when the phone rang and they instinctively looked at each other. They both knew who was ringing without telling each other. It was just eight o'clock as Charles picked up the phone in the bedroom.

"Evening, Charles Drought speaking."

"Good evening Mr Drought, Mr Pitter here again," he answered in that same irritating cheerful tone. "I will be brief. I want you to join the Atlantic Conveyor as senior third engineer at West Canada Dock tomorrow morning as early as possible after nine o'clock. I am sorry it's such short notice but that's the way the MoD work you know," he said.

"No I don't know how the MoD work," Charles gruffly replied.

"Ah no, well anyway, I would be obliged if you would contact another engineer who lives near you in Bebington and pass the same message on to him, he is ex-directory, I think you have sailed with him before, Mr Brian Williams."

Charles felt like telling Mr Pitter to get stuffed but he didn't. "Yes, I will get the message to him, Mr Pitter. Anything else you want me to do?" he enquired.

"No, that's all for the time being."

"Good night then," said Charles, and quickly put the phone down. This method of communication between head office and seagoing personnel was not unusual since Cunard had left Liverpool and relocated in London.

Charles turned round to face Betty. "Well love, that's our evening out to the 'Coach' up the Swanee. I have to join the 'Conveyor' first thing in the morning," he told her as calmly as he could muster.

This news really shattered Betty and she was too upset to talk, let alone reply coherently. She walked across the bedroom and took Charles into her arms and held him tight, burying her face into his shoulder hoping he could not see the distress this news had brought upon her, but Charles could feel her shaking uncontrollably inside her body. After a minute or two, having composed herself within the comfort of his embrace, she stood back and held him at arms length by his shoulders and looked straight into his eyes, and without a quiver in her voice bravely said, "Well Charles me boy, you had better start packing then."

Charles gave a little cough to clear the tightness in his throat in case any trace of emotion came into his voice. "I have to go and tell Brian Williams in Bebington. He is also required to join the 'Conveyor' along with me in the morning. I will have to go around to see John next door and ask him if he would kindly run us over in his car."

"No, I will go and ask him," said Betty. "You get started with your packing and don't forget anything."

After Betty had explained the circumstances to John, he readily agreed to take them to Bebington. They arrived at Brian's house only to find him out. Fortunately a neighbour was in and Charles asked him to ask Brian to ring him immediately he got back in. On their way back home Charles suggested they dropped into the Saughall Hotel for a quiet drink as a small compensation for missing out on their meal at the 'Coach'. There Betty expressed all her forebodings and misgivings about the forthcoming voyage. Charles did his best to quell her fears, but nothing that he said could lift this fear from her mind.

Back in the house, Charles went upstairs and finished his packing - a job he always did himself in case something was left behind and then he could only blame himself. While finishing his packing Brian Williams rang, and Charles passed on the message from Mr Pitter.

"You are a great pal giving me that news," Brian said laughingly. "Thanks anyway, I will come round in the morning in the car, about nine o'clock, and we will travel together to join her."

"That will be great," said Charles "I will be ready for you at nine."

Having completed his packing, he carried his large case down the stairs and left it in the hall by the front door and walked into the lounge. Betty was already sitting on the settee, and on the small occasional table stood a bottle of their favourite red wine and two of their best crystal glasses.

"Now there is a sight," exclaimed Charles. "A beautiful woman, a bottle of superb wine - not the Tesco plonk, and they are both for me. Aren't I the lucky one tonight," he said warmly.

"Don't be getting any ideas kiddo," she said with half a smile.

They talked aimlessly for a while about something and nothing, carefully choosing their words in case a slip of the tongue destroyed this moment of intimacy that does exist between husband and wife after many years of marriage.

Suddenly there was a pause in the talking. Charles leaned over and poured some more wine into their half empty glasses and took a sip from his.

"Betty, are you really worried about this trip?" he asked.

"Of course I am, I worry about every trip you go away on," she replied.

"I know that Betty, what I mean is, are you more worried than usual?"

"I suppose I am Charles. I can only think of the dangers you might sail into and of the worst things that may happen to you." Her voice was full of fear. Charles put his glass down and took her into his arms and kissed her tenderly, she was close to tears. Holding her tight he said, "Don't worry darling, nothing is going to happen to me. I love you too much to leave you for ever. I will come back in one piece, just you wait and see," he tried to assure her.

Betty pulled away from Charles and looked at him through moist filled eyes, frightened to blink in case a tear rolled down her cheek. "I love you too and I don't want you to leave me for ever either."

The only light in the room was from a table lamp that was behind her and it shone through her hair giving her an ethereal appearance. Charles had never seen her look so beautiful and he gazed at her in awe.

Betty took a deep breath and spoke quietly but firmly. "You are a good man Charles, I will pray for you every day and ask God to keep you safe from any dangers that might come your way. He will answer my prayers - I know he will. You will be all right, you will make it," and she smiled her lovely smile and Charles thought she looked more radiant than ever. He took her in his arms again and kissed her long and lovingly. Charles was deeply troubled. "I hope this will not be the last time I will ever hold her and kiss her," he said to himself.

Charles knew he must break this melancholy moment. He pulled away from Betty and said in his best, drunken voice, "How about another glass of wine, girl?" She smiled at him coyly. "Are you trying to get me drunk Charles Drought, so you can have your evil way with me?" she giggled. "I have not finished the second glass yet."

"Now whatever made you think of that," said Charles as he reached over the back of her and turned the table lamp off.

2

JOINING THE 'ATLANTIC CONVEYOR'

The next morning Charles hastily downed a cup of coffee and munched on a piece of toast while standing at the kitchen table. He did not feel like eating anything really. Brian Williams duly arrived at nine o'clock in his car - one thing Charles could always rely on was punctuality with Brian, having sailed with him before. He was a stickler for being on time. Charles's final goodbye to Betty was brief, they had said all they had to say the night before. He held her tight and kissed her, then turned away quickly and walked out of the door not daring to look back. He mumbled a perfunctory "Good morning" to Brian's wife sitting in the back of the car, afraid to say too much in case his voice betrayed his emotions. They drove away, Charles staring steadfastly ahead. He knew that Betty's face would be streaked with tears, and for him to have seen that would have broken his heart, knowing that it was him that was causing this pain and sorrow to the only person in the world he loved so deeply.

Charles and Brian hardly spoke a word to each other during the time it took to travel over to Liverpool, each one deep in their own thoughts of what could possibly lie ahead of them, and what they had let themselves in for. Mrs Williams, who was to drive the car back home, kept her silence, understanding only too well and respecting their need for silence. It was a melancholy journey. Charles had left the 'Conveyor' some eight or nine months ago and she had been laid up ever since. He did not relish the prospect of going on board a dead ship, especially after nine months; there is no more dispiriting or sadder sight than a vessel laid up in dock, just an inert hulk, dark and cold, no sound emanating from her, no movement of life on board, lying there big and lifeless like a beached dead whale.

They arrived alongside the 'Conveyor' in West Canada Dock at a little before 10 o'clock and were pleasantly surprised to be greeted with the sight of a hive of activity on and around the ship. People were scurrying about all over the place, lights blazing everywhere, blue flashes from welder's torches. It was a scene of great haste

They walked through the entrance doors on the side of the ship, dodging the workmen carrying tools and equipment, and down an alleyway past the open door to the engine room. They noticed that the preliminary procedure for lighting up the main boilers had already taken place.

"Saves us a job Brian," Charles joked as they made their way amidships. Suddenly Charles saw an old shipmate, Graham Ross, a second engineer he had sailed with previously.

"Hey there, Graham," he called out. "Where do you sign in on this bleedin' hotel."

"Hello Charlie," he said with genuine warmth. "I didn't expect to see you aboard here, I thought you were still on leave."

Charles winced, he hated being addressed as Charlie or Chas, and made a point of stressing this little idiosyncrasy to anyone who transgressed and mangled his Christian name, but on this occasion he held his tongue.

"You know the set up, Graham. When Herr Pitter calls it is not a request, it is an order," Charles said. "Anyway where and who do we report to?"

"You should know, you've sailed in her before. Go to the main saloon, all the big wigs are in there supping ale and smoking duty frees. You should find the engineers' superintendent somewhere in that lot."

Charles thanked Graham and promised to have a beer with him later, and made his way towards the main saloon. He pushed the doors open and his gaze met a room full of assorted characters, some in Naval uniform, some in boiler suits and others in dark suits. All were in deep conversation. As predicted by Graham, most of them had a glass filled with some kind of alcohol in one hand and a cigarette in the other. Across this smoke filled room they saw the superintendent engineer for Cunard from London. At that same time he saw Charles and Brian standing in the door way looking a little lost. He immediately broke off his conversation with the group of Naval officers and came across to them.

"Good morning, gentlemen, welcome aboard," he cordially greeted them. "Are you the new engineers joining the 'Conveyor'?"

"We are," they both replied simultaneously.

"Splendid, which one of you is Mr Drought?" he enquired.

"I am Sir," replied Charles.

"You have served on this vessel before I believe."

"Yes Sir," replied Charles.

"That's fine. You won't be wanting to be shown around the engine room then?"

"I doubt it Sir," said Charles.

"And you, Mr Williams, are familiar with this type of engine room, although you have not been aboard this particular vessel before?" the superintendent questioned.

"Indeed I am," Brian reassured him.

"Well, I can not express strongly enough that time is of the essence on board here. The Chief Engineer tells me there is a hell of lot of work to get through in such a short time to get the engines into something like top gear," he said. "So I would like both of you to get changed into your working clothes as soon as possible, get below and report to the Chief. We sail for Devonport on the p.m. tide tomorrow, all things being equal. Any questions gentlemen?"

This was the first intimation Charles had as to where they were going and when, and it left him a little taken aback by the swiftness of their imminent departure and why all the hurry. Charles thought for a moment, rubbing his chin, and came to the conclusion that a few devious questions might get him some of the answers to his troubled mind.

"Can we make any phone calls, or are we under any kind of censorship?" he queried.

"Make as many as you like. The phone is free on board and there is no censorship as yet," he cautioned.

"What about going ashore tonight?" Charles asked.

"You will have no time to go ashore tonight with the amount of work you have in front of you in the engine room," he said with a grin.

"Any other questions? I have to get back to those Naval chappies over there." Charles realised he was getting nowhere with his questions and decided just to find out what his duty times were to be.

"Only one more question Sir. When are the sea watches being set and what watch will I be on?"

"As senior third engineer you will be in charge of the eight to twelve watch starting tonight and you, Mr. Williams, will be on the four to eight watch with the second engineer," the superintendent answered. The superintendent, fearing other leading questions, abruptly turned on his heels and headed back across the smoke laden room.

"You need a bloody radar to see your way across that room," thought Charles. He shrugged his shoulders resignedly; he was none the wiser what the 'Conveyor's duty was going to be or where she was going after Devonport. He left the saloon and went to the same cabin he last occupied some months ago and quickly changed into his working gear and went down the iron stairways into the engine room.

Arriving at the bottom of the stairs he was met by the Chief Engineer, Jim Stewart, who hailed from Dundee. "Well, hello Charles, nice to see you again. Are you sailing with us?" he enquired as he shook Charles warmly by the hand.

"Thanks Chief. Yes, I will be sailing with you again on this trip."

"That's great. It's nice to have someone around the engine room you know and who knows what's what in the engine room. But I will tell you something, Charles me boy, there is sure some work down here to get this box of tricks ready for sea. I've heard we are expected to sail tomorrow p.m.," the Chief said anxiously, quite concerned he would not get all the work completed in time for sailing.

"That's what the Superintendent said up in the saloon, 'p.m. tide tomorrow', that's our deadline so we had better get down to it. We won't get anything done standing here yarning away," Charles said with half a smile. He liked the Chief immensely.

"You have not changed much, Charles, in your outlook towards work, have you, thank God," he said whimsically. "Right then, let's go and get to it, you know the set-up, no need for me to tell you what to do."

Charles worked all that day without a break, even for a cup of tea. Steam was raised, the two main turbines were warmed through, and eventually the whole of the engine room was humming like a Hornby train. Everything was ready for sailing by six p.m., in what was record time by any engine logbook. Sea watches were set and as Charles was not due on watch until eight p.m. he decided to have a lie down.

Although he was very tired - it had been a hectic, strenuous and emotional day - Charles found it hard to sleep, his mind continually racing from one dark thought to another and sleep would not come to him. He welcomed the knock on his cabin door and a voice announcing: "One bell Sir", indicating he had fifteen minutes before his watch commenced. He swung his long legs out over his bunk, walked to his bathroom, and splashed cold water all over his face and the back of his neck, cleaned his teeth and wearily climbed into his working gear once again. He relieved Graham, the second engineer, and quickly set about doing all the general tasks associated with a watch in port. Time hung heavily on his hands and his mind was constantly thinking of Betty and wondering what she would do or how she would cope if anything happened to him on this voyage. This problem had never entered his head before, this was a complete new situation he faced and he found it hard to deal with.

Charles could not rid himself of these morbid thoughts that kept invading his mind. He tried to shake them off by finding work however unnecessary it might be, but no matter how hard or complicated the tasks he undertook he could not lose this feeling that this could be his last trip forever. Even the pleasant surprise he had when he arrived in the engine room to find his second in command was Bill Czarnecky, a Polish engineer mechanic with whom he had sailed before and of whom he thought very highly, failed to raise his spirits. At last midnight arrived. Charles had never been so glad to hear 'eight bells', signalling the end of his watch, in all his life. He handed over the watch to the Fourth Engineer with the minimum of fuss and conversation, pleading tiredness for what may have been seen as unseemly and very abrupt, in his haste to leave the engine room, but Charles was utterly drained from all that had happened that day.

Within fifteen minutes of leaving the engine room he had showered and jumped into his bunk. He had momentarily thought he should complete his unpacking before turning in but he thought otherwise, a decision he would later bitterly regret. He laid down in his bunk with a long drawn out sigh of a tired and worried man, his last thoughts were of Betty as he fell into a deep and exhausted sleep.

3

THE CONVERSION TO
AN AIRCRAFT CARRIER

The next morning was equally hectic on board. Charles quickly ate his 'full monty' breakfast at seven bells and was down in the engine room with Bill the engineer mechanic at 0800hrs. There was still an enormous amount of preparatory work to be done, even though the other engineers had toiled all night, to get the engine room in perfect condition for sailing into unknown waters and to unknown destinations. Charles was becoming increasingly concerned with the conflicting reports from the ship's radio and the local newspapers about the Falkland situation. On the one hand US Secretary of State Haig and President Reagan were continuing to search for a peaceful solution, while on the other hand Maggie Thatcher was sabre rattling saying any aggression by Argentina must be overcome, and that she would use any force under her command to restore the Islands to British rule.

They continued to work until the Shipping Master came on board to attend the duties of signing on all the Officers and crew ready for the voyage. There were 32 crewmen, whose ages ranged from nineteen to their fifties. All were given the option to refuse to sign on but no one took this option up. Charles and Bill relieved each other to go up to the main saloon and duly sign on. It was very noticeable to Charles there was no mention of war bonuses or danger money which pleased him immensely.

"Maybe we are not going to enter the war zone after all," he wondered.

The crew were quickly allocated their watches and duties, and at six p.m. on April 16th the 'Atlantic Conveyor', under the guidance of a Liverpool Pilot and assisted by tugs, eased her way off the berth and sailed on that fateful voyage from Liverpool. As the 'Conveyor' sailed majestically down the Mersey, Charles stood on deck and took a long look at the familiar skyline as it slipped silently past and wondered if he would ever see it again. The Liverpool skyline, renowned throughout the world, had an almost magical effect on seamen from the North West who thought it was the world's most beautiful sight, but it brought with it very contrasting emotions. One of joy and exultation when inward bound and docking after a long voyage away, and sadness and heartache when sailing outward bound on another voyage of undetermined length. They took this image of the skyline with them wherever they sailed. It was an image that never faded nor could it be erased from their minds. It was this vision of the 'Skyline of Heaven', as it was always called, that kept northwest seamen going against all adversities in war and peace.

The mayhem during the conversion of the Atlantic Conveyor
into an aircraft carrier at Devonport

The passage to Devonport was uneventful, just the usual few niggling shakedown problems always expected when bringing a ship out from being laid up, but nothing that the engineers could not cope with. Charles slipped easily into the watch routine, and the stress he had been feeling eased a little with no talk of danger money being discussed by anyone.

Along with Charles, most of the crew felt the 'Conveyor' would in all probability be used for ferrying supplies from the UK to the Ascension Islands in the south Atlantic, and they were all feeling a little bit less apprehensive of the forthcoming months. In the last phone call Charles made to Betty before they sailed from Liverpool he told her of the general feeling of everyone on board in an effort to allay her fears which he fervently hoped it would.

They docked in Devonport on the evening of April 17th. The following morning all hell broke loose, dockyard workers swarmed like ants all over the ship and the noise of their work, day and night, was horrendous. In the accommodation area of the ship there was just as much noise and activity as various cabins were taken over by the military and hastily converted. The cabin next to Charles's was normally the 2nd Officer's and it was being altered so that it would accommodate twelve personnel. Charles at first felt rather embarrassed being on his own in such a spacious cabin when in the same space next door twelve people would be crammed in with all their gear. He soon shrugged that feeling off because he knew full well the rule was that all watch keeping officers must have a cabin to themselves.

The main noise and disturbance came from the workers using pneumatic tools as they cleared the Main Deck of eye pads and container stools. Charles stayed on watch, as did all the engine room staff, the whole time this pandemonium reigned, and only cat-napped during the brief periods off watch. It was impossible to get a good sleep with all that was going on around him. The clearing of the main deck of all obstructions was the first inkling that Charles had that the 'Conveyor' was not going to be used just to ferry equipment to and fro from the UK, and his fears were confirmed the next day when an official memo was posted on the Daily News board in the officer's lounge. This stated that the 'Conveyor' was to be converted for use as an aircraft carrier to take on Harrier aircraft to supplement any losses which may be sustained by any subsequent action by the Task Force in the Falklands.

This news disturbed Charles's thoughts and that night on watch he voiced his concern to Bill, his second in command. "Did you see that notice in the lounge, Bill, telling us that we are to be converted into an aircraft carrier?" he asked.

"No I didn't, I have not been in there to-day," he replied.

"Well we are going to carry Harrier Jets as back-ups in case they lose any front line jets in action. What do you think of that then?"

Before Bill could answer the Chief Engineer arrived in the engine room. "Good evening Charles, Bill," he nodded to them both. "You have probably heard or read the news about what is going to happen to the 'Conveyor'. It has come as quite a surprise to me as no doubt it has to you, so the news I bring won't surprise you all that much."

"I have been informed that our voyage length will be indefinite, so quite obviously with that sort of time scale fresh water is going to be a problem. With no means of replenishing from an outside source, fresh water will be at a premium, and another thing, we will be carrying possibly 200 extra personnel for most of the voyage, if not all of the voyage. Do you follow my line of thinking?" he asked.

Charles and Bill both nodded in assent and wondered what was coming next.

The Second Officer's cabin converted to accommodate twelve personnel.

"Our main task at this time," the Chief continued, "is to ensure that our two evaporation plants are in tip top working order so the two high pressure boilers are kept with a plentiful supply of pure distilled water to drive the turbines, OK?" he questioned, not expecting an answer from two well versed engineers he knew so well.

"To make matters even more complicated we will have on board an extra 200 personnel. You already know we have a fresh water sanitary system, but on top of this, fresh water will be needed for normal washing and cooking facilities for these extra blokes. A right bloody headache this is going to be, I am sure," said the Chief exasperatedly.

"How are we going to get round this problem Chief?" Charles asked anxiously.

The Chief paused for a moment. "Well, in the first place, in an attempt to cut down on the use of fresh water for sanitary purposes, I have arranged with the MoD to install at various points on one side of the main deck metal troughs with a drain hole leading over the side to be used by the deck crew and military personnel whenever they want to have a quick pee. That should save a fair amount of water not having to flush the bogs every time they have a squirt," the Chief said rather proudly of his idea of saving water.

"Good idea Chief, but it's going to be a bit difficult if it's the weather side and we start shipping seas. It is the Atlantic we will be in, not on a lake in Windermere," Charles replied with a laugh.

"In that case they will have to just tie a knot in it and wait until the weather calms down," answered the Chief, and they all laughed together envisaging the scene of bulging bladders.

When all these temporary conveniences had been fitted, true to form, the MoD demanded that they be inspected and passed by a Royal Navy officer. Charles had just come off watch at noon and he had come up on to the main deck for a bit of fresh air when he was suddenly confronted by a rather resplendent naval officer, all gold braid and brass buttons.

"Good afternoon old chap, are you a ship's engineer?" he addressed Charles in a rich plummy voice so beloved in the Royal Navy.

"I am one of them indeed," replied Charles, trying hard not to smile.

"Excellent, I have been sent to see the new urinal. Have you any idea where it is?"

Charles could not resist the old hoary Liverpool dockers joke. "The urinal sir, can you tell me how many funnels she has got?"

The young officer looked perplexed for a moment or two, frowning at Charles and then his face slowly broke into a smile.

"Sorry about that, old chap. Let me rephrase that." He gave a little cough. "I have been sent by the MoD to inspect the troughs our chaps are going to use during the voyage whenever they wish to discharge their forepeaks."

"Right, I understand now what you want to do."

They both appreciated the humour of the situation. Charles showed him around all the newly installed troughs, they must have been suitable and up to MoD standard because he made no adverse comments - in fact he made no comments at all. When the inspection was finished he shook Charles's hand and thanked him profusely for his time and trouble in showing him around. His last words to Charles as he left the ship were, "I say, old boy, I am going to get some mileage out of that 'How many funnels has she got remark'."

Charles went down to his cabin and decided that before he went to lunch he would complete his unpacking and put everything neatly away. He was extremely meticulous over his unpacking. With space being at a premium in his cabin, every article had a specific place to go. Charles had nearly finished his unpacking when he suddenly discovered he had not packed any change of underwear, all he had was what he was wearing at this moment. He swore under his breath and then he panicked. "If I have forgotten to pack such an important item as underwear what else could I have forgotten?" he thought. Suddenly he realised he had not seen his Bible that he treasured so much. It had been a gift from his father on his first trip to sea. He always carried it with him on every voyage, and to Charles it acted as a talisman to bring him good luck and keep him safe from all evil. Frantically he searched every inch of his luggage for the Bible but to his utter mortification he failed to find it and he realised that he had also left his precious Bible at home.

Charles was inconsolable, he slumped down into a chair leant forward and buried his head into his hands. "How the hell could I have forgotten my Bible?" He wondered if this was an omen or portent of some grave significance of what lay ahead of him in the coming weeks. He was so distraught he could not face going to lunch. He quickly showered and slipped into his bunk and lay there in a bleak mood, once again his mind racing, thinking of all the terrible things that could happen to him without the protection of his Bible. Eventually sleep overtook his troubled mind. He was awakened by the steward with his afternoon tea which he hurriedly consumed and quickly went ashore to the NAFFI on 'H.M.S. Drake' to replenish his stock of underwear at an exorbitant price and a hideous style. "Beggars can't be choosers," he muttered, eyeing up the offending garments.

'Atlantic Conveyor', GR. Ton 14,950. Cunard Steamship Co. Ltd,
after her complete refit. Lost to exocet missiles May 25th 1982.
Position 51° 07 S 55° 27 W. 12 Crew members killed.

4

LEAVING ENGLAND

Whilst Charles wrestled with his own personal problems on the 'Conveyor', he heard that the House of Commons had reassembled in the middle of their Easter recess to hear the Prime Minister report on the present state of play in the Falklands dispute, and to debate the crisis. Mrs Thatcher's rhetoric that "Wherever naked aggression occurs it must be overcome, the cost, however high, must be set against the cost we would one day have to pay if this principle went by default", convinced Charles this trip was not going to be a pleasure cruise by any stretch of the imagination.

He aired his feelings to the other engineers during a short tea break.

"It's all right for them to be mouthing off about overcoming aggression no matter what the cost," he said. "They will be thousands of miles away sipping gin and tonics in the Commons bar while us poor bastards face all the flak the Argies can throw at us."

"It's not sure yet if there will be any wa," someone said.

"Ha! Don't hold your breath on that assumption. They want a war for more reasons than getting the Falklands back," Charles scornfully answered. Before any more discussion could take place the tea break ended and they returned to their respective duties.

At last, after eight days of indescribable dirt and noise, all the repairs and alterations were completed and the 'Conveyor' was made ready for sea. The vessel was scheduled to move out to anchor in the Plymouth Sound early in the evening of April 26th. Charles made one last phone call to Betty under strict instructions not to mention any alterations to the ship, its intended use, or its movements. He also refrained from telling her what he had forgotten to bring away with him. The telephone was removed from the ship that afternoon of the 26th, all shore leave was cancelled, and a strict censorship was imposed on all the final letters any of the crew on board had written. It was at this point of time that all personnel on board were informed that from now on the 'Atlantic Conveyor' would only be referred to as N.P. 1840 (Naval Party 1840).

'Atlantic Conveyor' ready to sail full loaded with
Sea King and Chinook helicopters and other implements of war

At 1800hrs the 'Atlantic Conveyor' eased herself out of the docks, ably assisted by the Admiralty tugs, and made her way to the anchorage in the Plymouth Sound. There were thousands of people on all the vantage points surrounding the Sound. All were cheering and waving Union Flags. "Such a contrast to leaving Liverpool where no one came down to the berth to see us leave, no cheering crowds, no waving of flags, just a few dockers and the Lock Master and his crew on Canada Dock - what a difference," thought Charles.

He and other engineers had come on deck to watch the departure. "So much for all the hush-hush and censorship about our leaving," said Charles to the others. "Old Maggie Thatcher is bloody marvellous at keeping her mouth shut," he snorted. They all agreed with Charles, but he found the cheering crowds quite moving. He turned to face his fellow engineers.

"Well lads, we cannot come to much harm with all these people thinking and praying for us can we?" They looked hard at him. Some nodded, some just shrugged their shoulders, but no-one spoke in reply. It was an eerie silence that greeted his statement. Charles heaved a heavy sigh, turned on his heels and went back to his cabin.

The main reason for anchoring in the Sound was for the testing of the hastily constructed flight decks, forward and aft. The after flight deck was only used by the Chinook and Wessex Five type helicopters, the forward flight deck was reserved totally for the Sea Harriers. The Chinook helicopters all flew on board along with the much smaller Wessex Five type. Some of these Wessex were to remain in permanent use whilst others were stored on deck with folded rotors. There were even more Wessex in crates stored below decks.

Charles was amazed at the very impressive and diverse array of military hardware above and below decks. There was a portable runway and rows and rows of trolleys loaded with tents and marquees or, as it was explained to him, a 'tented city'. There were numerous army vehicles and even steel shallow bottomed boats. There was not a single empty space available even the after end of B Deck had been converted into a workshop for the repair of aircraft, mainly helicopters, damaged in the forthcoming conflict. Nothing was left to chance, but not quite all.

It was very disturbing for Charles to see how a peacetime Merchant ship could be so quickly and easily converted into an instrument for war. What his greatest concern was that they would obviously be sailing into a potential war situation with attacks coming from the skies and possibly the sea. The Argentineans did have a Navy which included an Aircraft Carrier, and yet no armaments of any kind had been fitted to the "Conveyor" to repel any hostile attack from land, sea or air. This lack of any defensive equipment on board greatly troubled Charles.

Charles was lucky enough to be off duty on Sunday lunch time. He was having a pre-lunch drink and was standing looking through the forward facing windows of the officers lounge when he was treated to an awe aspiring sight of a Sea Harrier flying in, firstly from the starboard side, stopping in mid-air about twenty feet above the deck, rotating a complete circle until its nose faced him, and landing perfectly and gently on the flight deck. The Harrier then flew off only to return and execute the whole manoeuvre just as perfectly from the port side. These trials greatly impressed Charles.

By 1700hrs on Sunday April 26th all the trials and preparations had been completed and all extra personnel had been boarded. The 'Conveyor' weighed anchor and proceeded out of Plymouth Sound and into the English Channel. The 'Conveyor' was under the command of Captain Ian North. He was a very experienced Master, and the first Master in the ACL company to win the much-coveted gold-headed cane for bringing the first ship into Montreal Harbour after the winter ice had dispersed whilst he was in command of the 'Atlantic Prosper'. Captain North was everyone's image of what a British Captain should look like, with his neatly trimmed beard and commanding stature. He was a brilliant and fearless Master who did not suffer fools gladly, but was scrupulously fair to all under his command. Charles had sailed with him before and thought very highly of his competence as a Master. If there were any other Captain he would have chosen to be in command on such a voyage as this he could not recall one.

Cunard likewise regarded Captain North as one of their finest Masters, a Master to whom Cunard always turned when the introduction of a new type of ship, a new service, or anything out of the ordinary was planned. The requisition of the 'Conveyor' was such a situation ready made for Captain North to be called upon by Cunard. The 57-year-old bachelor from

Doncaster, who first went to sea at the age of 14 in 1939, was put on 48hrs notice to join the ship. Captain North, like everyone else, had little idea the part his 12 year-old ship would play in the Falklands War.

Just before Charles went below to start his watch he came up to the main deck and gazed out over the sea at the English coast line, slowly slipping past and he heaved a great sigh. He could not rid himself of the feeling that they were going, and for what reason, and, having no defences whatsoever against any form of hostile attack, there was a great possibility that he might never see England again or his dear wife.

He sensed someone had come on deck and stood behind him. He turned round and saw that it was Bill. He too was staring intently at the coastline with a deep frown on his brow.

"Are you thinking what I am thinking Bill?"

Bill just nodded and said nothing; they instinctively knew each other's thoughts. They stood together a little while longer and then without another word turned around and went below to start their watch.

Captain Ian North 1925 - 1982
Master 'Atlantic Conveyor'
Fondly referred to as 'Captain Birdseye' throughout the Cunard Fleet.

5

THE FREETOWN EXPERIENCE

Charles dropped into the routine of watches, meal times and sleep at sea quite easily - he always did, but on this voyage everyone had to work a few extra hours either before or after their watch. Charles chose to work the extra duty during the afternoon, usually from 1pm until 3pm. It suited his life long habits at sea. He could still have a short nap in the afternoon, and more importantly he would still be able to indulge in the social chat with the pre-dinner drink in the evening,

Charles had hoped that once at sea away from the mayhem and hubbub of the Admiralty Ship Yard it would become the usual peaceful voyage with not a lot to do even with the compulsory extra hours of duty. These hopes were soon to be shattered. The first disruption to a peaceful trip came when the first standard lifeboat and emergency drills took place a day after leaving Devonport. The ship's crew performed their normal drill to perfection as would be expected of highly trained Merchant seamen, but the military performed their own ideas of a lifeboat and emergency drill. The result was utter chaos and a complete disaster. It was decided there and then that some sort of coalition lifeboat and emergency drill must be instituted between the two parties. This meant Charles had to spend a large amount of his valuable rest time practising lifeboat and emergency drill with the military personnel, which irked him immensely. Eventually this coalition drill, after innumerable attempts to get it right, did work efficiently and it was to prove invaluable.

The next unsuspected interruption to Charles's hopeful peaceful existence came when they had to rendezvous with the Royal Fleet Auxiliary Tanker 'Grey Rover' for the purpose of rehearsing taking on board oil fuel bunkers whilst underway at sea. To the engineers on the 'Conveyor' this was an entirely new innovation. They became heavily involved in this manoeuvre, and although it eroded more of Charles's off duty time, he thoroughly enjoyed it. To him it was exciting doing something for the first time, and he had a great sense of accomplishment when the re-fuelling was completed without a drop being spilt, and in the fastest time. He was that sort of dedicated engineer.

A. F. A. 'Grey Rover' fleet oil-refueling vessel

Refueling at full speed. A manouevre fraught with danger.

Two days later they met the requisitioned Townsend Thoreson ferry m.v. 'Europic Ferry', and the speed of the 'Conveyor' had to be adjusted to that of the ferry, which was a much slower vessel as they continued to proceed south. That evening when Charles came on watch he was surprised to see the Chief in the engine room.

"Evening Charles, heard the news?" he asked.

"Nope," replied Charles airily.

"We are bound for Freetown."

"What?" exclaimed Charles. "Freetown, what a hole of a place. If the world had piles Freetown is the place they would be."

"I know. The last time I bunkered a ship there it took days, not hours. They could only bunker at two tons an hour and we had every conceivable breakdown you could imagine during the bunkering. It was hell, I tell you. And another annoying thing, we never got the right amount of fuel we needed but we were charged for it, the robbing bastards" the Chief gloomily said.

"You are right about being robbing bastards. When we docked there last time, we soon learned to keep our doors locked and just use a port hole for air, otherwise the 'crew boys' from ashore would pinch everything moveable in sight in your room," Charles rejoined.

In their sea going careers they both had had first hand experience on other vessels, off the West Coast of Africa, especially Freetown, which was usually the first and last port to call into when trading on that coast. Charles had got to know Freetown fairly well with its teeming streets, the sweaty heat, the noisy yelling locals, the torrential downpours during the rainy season and the debilitating humidity, during a spell sailing with the Guinea Gulf Line, a shipping company that had a regular trade to the West Coast of Africa and he had sworn never, but never, to return to that God forsaken spot again.

Charles began to reminisce. "On the subject of robbing bastards, I particularly remember one trip I did. We had taken the usual mob of evil smelling 'crew boys' on board in Freetown and ensconced them on the two forward hatches and rigged up two tarpaulin hatch covers to serve as a tent over them. We used to call it the 'Freetown Hilton'," Charles said laughingly. "They were the usual villainous looking lot - most 'crew boys" were - but this bunch looked more so than the usual run of the mill 'pirates' who worked on our ships to handle the loading and discharging of our cargoes as we sailed around the coast and up the creeks. The first thing the First Mate did when he saw this crowd coming aboard was to order the 'Chippy' to unscrew and remove all the sounding pipe caps about the decks and replace them with wooden plugs. As you know, Chief, they were made of solid brass and were regarded as prize items for those buggers to swipe. At the same time he ordered the Bosun to remove any loose metal or metal that could be removed, and any chain work that was about the decks and stow it away in a safe place, he was taking no chances."

The Chief nodded sagely, agreeing with everything Charles was saying. Charles was now in full verbal flow. "Well, we sailed up one of the creeks to a place called Warri, another God forsaken spot, and on the first night in the Second Mate had gone to bed. He had locked his door and put the port holes on the deadlocks. He had done everything to make his cabin secure while he slept, or so he thought. Now this you have got to believe, it's the gospel truth Chief. Sometime during the night some of the 'crew boys' managed to get into his cabin while he slept, and without disturbing him stripped the cabin bare of everything removable. They took his sextant and binoculars that, ironically, he had brought down from the chart room for safe keeping, and do you know what? This is the most amazing thing. They lifted him up off his bunk and stole the mattress and the sheets from under him without even waking him. Can you believe that?" asked Charles.

"I believe you Charles," replied the Chief. "I have heard tales of such going on down on the West Coast. It is hard to believe but it does happen."

"Well, the poor old Second Mate had only the pyjamas he was sleeping in, everything else had been swiped by those thieving bastards. To this day he swears that they must have pumped some sort of gas into his room, through the key hole perhaps, to knock him out and it made him sleep so soundly that he did not feel them lift him to pinch his mattress from underneath him, or hear them stripping his room. He said he had woken up with a thundering headache, something he never has, and this convinced him even more that he had been somehow drugged. How they got into his cabin he never found out, there were no signs of a forced entry," concluded Charles.

"Amazing," the Chief said, "just amazing."

"Yes, and now we are going back to that hell hole of a place called Freetown. Someone up there must really hate us," said Charles, pointing skywards with a grimace.

'Atlantic Conveyor' Steaming in the fetid heat towards Freetown

"Aye, could be, but listen. Have you thought of this, the 'Conveyor' has never been south of the equator before, or indeed ever been in the tropics. She was never built for that trade, and here we are heading for Freetown without any proper tropical ventilation. You know Charles, we are going to roast down in the engine room. It will be like an oven down there."

"Why the hell didn't the MoD pick up on the fact she had always traded on the North Atlantic routes, and fit us with some sort of air conditioning?" Charles said grievously.

"God only knows, don't ask me why. I am only the poor bloody Chief Engineer. They tell me sod all," he complained. "Right ho, I am off. Have a good watch Charles, see you in the morning no doubt." He turned and made his way out of the engine room, leaving Charles to contemplate on the forthcoming furnace that was to become the engine room.

One of the sights that never failed to impress Charles and gave him a great deal of pleasure was to see the helicopters practising take off and landings and lifting different weighted loads off the deck of the 'Conveyor'. Whenever the flying stations were in operation the engine room was always in a full state of readiness in case an order came to increase or decrease engine revolutions. Charles accepted the extra responsibility and work just for the joy of watching these operations during his off watch periods.

These flying operations were not without their dangers. On one or two occasions there was a spillage of aviation fluid, known as 'Avcat', on the forward deck and with these spillages there was a very high risk of a serious fire. Consequently the fire pumps were always kept in a state or readiness in the engine room, to be activated at a moments notice during these flying operations. The Military had one hell of a job clearing the decks of the 'Avcat' spillages.

'Europic Ferry' GR Ton 4,190 sailed with the 'Atlantic Conveyor' to Freetown

The two ships proceeded southwards, steaming through the hot hushed glass-like surface of the sea, and the weather became increasingly hot by the day, much to the consternation and discomfort of the engineers. Charles's nose had already told him from the dust-dry smell and a sort of musty smell that he occasionally picked up out of the air that they were approaching the African Coast, long before any land was in sight. He knew that smell only too well.

The Deck Office had been converted into a news room, and from there they printed a newspaper which was a condensed version of the current news from home and abroad. Charles found this very interesting and helpful, keeping him up with world events, as there was precious little time to listen to the radio with all the extra work that had been thrown on to the engineers.

The day before the 'Conveyor' arrived in Freetown a notice was placed on the news board warning all ship's personnel not to discuss the ship's destination or its cargo to anyone at all from ashore in Sierra Leone, and furthermore, all flying operations would be cancelled until further notice. Charles read these missives with some trepidation.

"It's getting that serious then," he said to himself. "Censorship coming in so early and we still don't know yet what our real purpose is going to be, but it sure looks as if we could be involved in the thick of it down there."

The approach into Freetown Harbour was slow and cautious due to the host of small vessels of home made dug out fishing canoes whose operators never gave way to any ship, no matter how big or what they were. Charles was relieved to hear from the Chief that their stay would be brief, only a day, but what a sweltering and hectic day it turned out to be. Whilst in port for that one day the Captain decided it would be a good idea to hold a full regulation fire and boat drill, remembering the total disaster the first practice drill had ended in. The Third Officer was in charge of one of the life-boats, assisted by a quartermaster of some years standing. They all assembled at their life-boat station and the life-boat was swung out board, Charles, with the lowering boat crew, climbed into the life-boat which was then lowered by its davits into the water without a hitch.

The remaining boat's crew then scrambled down the nets and ropes into the life-boat and they cast off. The mayhem was about to start, the crew of the life-boat consisted of stewards, cooks, mess-boys and military personnel - a right motley collection. Charles was squatting aft on a thwart, immaculate in white shorts and shirt and white shoes and socks. The order was given to up oars and lower them into the rowlocks - what a shambles it became. The Third Officer, tiller in hand, was shouting orders nobody understood, trying to get them to pull on the oars together, but they waved their oars around and 'caught crabs' the like of which nobody had ever seen before. They were having a grand old time of it. Eventually, the Third Officer gave up the unequal struggle to co-ordinate any type of a rowing rhythm and struggled back to the ship's side, fervently praying that they would never have to take to the boats in the foreseeable future.

Once back on board Charles was called into the engine room to assist in the bunkering of oil fuel and he found this particularly trying.

"There's no bloody air down here," he said to the Chief, "and I have found out where all the hot spots are."

"You're right, but the worst part for me, and I am sure it is for you as well, is that bleeding ladder up to the Engine Control Room Door."

"I know, those handrails are as hot as hell. They are almost untouchable," Charles bemoaned.

They sweated out the bunkering procedure with all the usual load of foul-ups from the shore installations, but both Charles and the Chief had anticipated these upsets from previous bunkering experiences in Freetown. They lethargically went about their duties, trying not to move too often, as this only brought on another spasm of uncontrollable perspiring. At last the bunkering nightmare ended and Charles went up on deck with Bill, leaving the Chief to do all the paperwork involved in the bunkering, but there was little or no respite from the suffocating heat.

To add to their discomfort, the heavy atmosphere brought the rotting smells of Freetown to their nostrils, and the ever-present mosquitoes began to home in on them. They hurriedly left the top deck to the safety of Charles's cabin, but could not escape the ever present heat and humidity because of the lack of air conditioning. These conditions did nothing to improve their tempers or their discontentment of the whole voyage.

Once in the cabin Charles broke open a case of lager and handed Bill a can. "Cheers," said Charles rather lacklustrely and took a long gulp. "Even the bloody ale is warm and I hate warm ale," Bill testily complained.

"Ah yes, but it is free, thanks to the MoD," smiled Charles.

"Thank God for small mercies," Bill answered. "Pity they didn't think of putting a fridge for the beer on board at the same time they put the beer on board, but that would have been too sensible for their tiny minds."

They both heaved a sigh of resignation, looked at each other, smiled at each other and without a word Charles raised an eyebrow in a questioning manner. "And why not," said Bill, and they both opened another can of lager. They sank a few more cans without any great relish, warm beer is far from refreshing and they sweated a bit more. Bill stood up, dumped his empty beer can into the waste basket and said, "Well Charles, I am off for a shower then my bunk."

"Me too," replied Charles. "See you in the morning. At least we will not have to spend another day in this arsehole of a place. Goodnight Bill."

6

SAILING FOR THE
ASCENSION ISLANDS

On the morning of May 2nd, at 0700hrs, the windlass on the forecastle head of the 'Conveyor' rattled, struggled and groaned hauling inboard all the mooring ropes and wires. When all the mooring forward and aft had been cleared, the engine room telegraph rang slow ahead and she swung around to starboard. As the 'Conveyor' slowly gathered speed she sounded three long blasts on her whistle, an age old custom of saying goodbye to the port you are leaving. The poor old 'Europic Ferry' had to remain behind and continue suffering the heat and fetid atmosphere of Freetown. The 'Conveyor' steamed sedately away from the shimmering heat, even at that time in the morning, and the fetid odour of a pungent mixture of bilge water, charcoal fires, rotting garbage, animal dung, unwashed humanity and local cooking: the general smell of the West Coast of Africa and in particular Freetown.

Charles was never so glad to leave a port as he was that morning, and as they proceeded at full speed southwards towards Ascension Island a more relaxed atmosphere came over all on board. It would be the last time such an atmosphere would prevail over the ship. During this part of the voyage the usual 'Crossing the Line' (Equator) ceremony was strictly observed, and Charles enthusiastically took part in initiating all the miscreants who had been unfortunate not to have crossed the equator before. Charles had volunteered to be one of King Neptune's helpers, a job he really relished.

There was one notable exception. A Naval Petty Officer had hidden away somewhere, and search as they did he could not be found. He was duly marked down to be double done on the homeward run northwards. This, as time will tell, never materialised.

Transferring supplies (vertrepping) at sea by Sea King helicopter on the after deck

The sea harriers' landing pad forwards.

A more important event had occurred for Charles and Bill. They had managed by many devious tactics to get their beloved lager refrigerated, even though it had cost them a case of lager or two as a payment for this privilege, but it was well worth it for the thirst quenching iced lager in the tropics.

Another important event occurred for Charles and all the civilian crew when they had crossed the line of latitude 6 South. Their pay was increased 150% as a war bonus. Some of the Military personnel were a little aggrieved at this bonanza to the crew, so in deference to them Charles and Co. played this increase down (Authors note: see end of book for amounts).

The 'Conveyor' arrived at Ascension Island during the early hours of the morning of May 4th and, as there are no berthing facilities on the island, the 'Conveyor' had to just drift off the island. Charles awoke at 0630hrs, dressed and hurried on deck. He had never been to the Ascension Island before and any new port always interested him immensely. As Charles stepped out on deck he was met with a grey and heavily overcast sky and it was raining heavily, the island was shrouded in mist and it was quite cool.

"Better than Freetown any day and any weather, even if it was snowing," said Charles to himself.

As he stood there he watched one of the large Chinook helicopters being expertly bladed up, and soon it took off for the island where it and its crew were to remain permanently. Charles shivered a little in the damp cool morning air and decided to go below for the early breakfast and ready himself for his watch. From time to time during his watch that morning Charles was able to come up from the engine room, leaving Bill to oversee the engines. It gave him a great deal of pleasure to see quite a lot of cargo being ferried ashore by helicopter, and the highly professional manner it was carried out. The stern ramp of the ship had been lowered and the helicopters winched the cargo up from there as it was brought out from inside the ship.

"A very smooth operation," mused Charles.

During the afternoon the weather cleared and Charles strolled around the deck with Bill watching all that was going on.

The Task Force

H. M. S. Sir Lancelot. Logistic Landing Ship

'Elk' Ro-Ro Cargo Supply Ship

H. M. S. Fearless Assault Ship

'Norland' The first merchant ship into San Carlos Bay.
H. M. S. Antelope sinks in the background

"Plenty of other ships here," Charles remarked to Bill. "That's the P&O job the 'Canberra', pointing out a large white passenger ship hove-to on the starboard side. "She will be carrying most of the troops, no doubt and look, there is the North Sea ferry the 'Norland'. Where did she appear from?"

Bill joined in the ship spotting game. "Over here on the port side, that large purpose built roll-on/roll-off ship is the 'Elk'. She can really carry a hefty load."

"I see the Navy has arrived," remarked Charles. "There are the assault ships 'HMS Fearless' and 'HMS Intrepid'. Quite a little gathering don't you think, for what is supposed to be a little excursion in the South Atlantic."

"Its quite impressive and worrying," agreed Bill.

"You know what really worries me, Bill?"

"No, what?"

"Those assault ships have a total manpower available on board of over 100 crew, and we have a measly 40. Mind you, running a Merchant ship and taking a warship into battle are two bloody different propositions. Warships are built differently and need duplication of every rank in case of injury or even worse, loss of life. Nevertheless, we, with our small crew, may still have to take the 'Conveyor' into the self-same battle zone. That is what worries me, does it you Bill?"

Bill remained silent for a while, frowning heavily in thought. "Well Charles, the way you put it, one can only be worried about the whole situation we could sail into." Bill shivered inwardly, thinking of the worst that could happen. They both looked at each other, nodded, turned and went off deck to their cabins, both deep in their own morbid thoughts.

All the following day was completely occupied by the landing and stowing of fourteen RAF and Naval Sea Harriers, the majority were the Naval Harriers. Two Harriers were safely stowed on the foredeck between the walls of the containers, which were down the outermost side of the deck so they performed an effective shelter for them. All the planes were covered in protective polythene. This was especially important for the RAF planes which were not treated with anti-corrosive against salt spray. The ship was now jam packed with lethal weapons of destruction for war, all heavily armed with tons of explosives stowed below decks. Charles viewed this situation with some trepidation. "Dear God, if we ever get hit we will go up like a rocket, and we have got sod all to protect us from getting hit." he bitterly thought.

On the evening of May 5th the Assault Group, as it was now called, sailed from Ascension led by the two HM ships the 'Fearless' and the 'Intrepid'. They sailed in station, with the 'Canberra' on the starboard side of the 'Conveyor' and the 'Elk' on the port side. Charles stood on deck and watched as the Assault Group left. There were ships to be seen, steaming along, as far as the horizon. The weather was calm and warm and the setting sun gave the few clouds in an otherwise cloudless sky a golden border, and silhouetted all the ships in the convoy against the still blue waters of the sea.

"What a glorious picture," thought Charles. "If only this majestic sight was for any other reason than the mission we are going on." But for all his misgivings about this mission and his concern about what the outcome might be, it was a most impressive sight to Charles and he could not help but be moved at the sight of this armada.

<u>The Race to the relief of the Falkland Islands</u>

H. M. S. Hermes and Broadsword in close formation

H. M. S. Invincible, leaving Portsmouth.

7

TOWARDS THE BATTLE ZONE

The eventual destination of the Assault Group was a rendezvous with the main task force somewhere at sea. There had been a very 'laid back' approach to this voyage so far. To Charles it was all so different, something out of the ordinary routine of being on watch as an engineer at sea, and he revelled in this experience. Everyone on board had the feeling that the peace negotiations would be successful and that the Argentineans would realise the hopelessness of their position against such highly trained forces from Britain, and by the time the 'Conveyor' got there it would be all over, and they would turn round and head back for the U.K.

As the Assault Group steamed south Charles's work on watch became increasingly busy. It was very important that the 'Conveyor' maintained her station in the convoy and this meant that the two engines could not exceed more than 90rpm, and often the engine room was ordered to reduce the revs as low as 40 or 50rpm to accommodate the helicopters that flew on and off the vessel all day, and often at night as well. These frequent journeys of the helicopters that placed so much extra strain on the engineers, to and fro from other vessels was called in naval jargon, 'vertrepping' (vertical replenishment at sea). Charles called them an effing nuisance. On top of this constant standby for altering the revs, every other day they took on oil fuel from a Fleet Tanker.

However, these journeyings of the helicopters always brought new faces on to the 'Conveyor'. Usually it was around lunch or dinnertime - the 'Conveyor' had a reputation as a good feeding ship for they had three Cunard chefs doing all the cooking. Charles revelled in the presence of new company as did most of the officers aboard the 'Conveyor', and he spent many pleasant hours listening to and relating stories of happenings while they had been at sea and ashore in foreign lands. Many a case of ice cold lager helped the story telling along. It was an age-old custom beloved of all seafarers.

On the second day out of Ascension, just before dinner, Charles, Bill and a few helicopter guests were having the usual 'happy hour' drink prior to dinner and a good chat with each other. They all felt very relaxed as they talked and laughed at one another's stories, but this cosy atmosphere was sensationally shattered. Over the ship's public address system Captain Layard, a Royal Naval Captain who made nightly broadcasts of events at home and in the Falklands, called for the attention of all the ships personnel and announced that 'HMS Sheffield' had been struck by an Exocet missile, set on fire, and had to be abandoned with the loss of many lives. This sudden and tragic news stunned them all and suddenly they realised, unbelievably, that they were in a war situation and they were steaming straight towards it.

There was a deep hushed silence as they all digested this terrible news. Bill was first to break the silence and voiced what all those on board were undoubtedly thinking. "Bloody hell, if those bastard Argies can sink one of our HM ships what chance have we got?"

"What in God's name is an Exocet?" exclaimed Charles.

"Haven't got a bloody clue," Bill answered.

"I have never heard of an Exocet missile either," said the Chief. "And listen, if one of those missiles can clobber the 'Sheffield', with all its sophisticated detection equipment and latest defensive weaponry, we have not got a cat in hell's chance of surviving against an attack by an Exocet."

"Another thing," interposed Charles, "don't forget we have no watertight compartments on the ship and, more importantly, no defences against any attack at all, be it a missile or an air attack."

"You know what we are," the Chief said bitterly, "we are bloody sitting ducks, that's what we are. With all our priceless cargo of Harriers and all that military hardware in the car decks we sure would make a valuable war prize for some Argie to sink us." They sat in silence reflecting on this gloomy scenario painted by the Chief.

With a heavy sigh Charles got out of his seat, leaving the remains of his drink on the table, too disturbed to continue drinking and announced, "Well, I am off for my dinner, anyone else coming?" The rest of the people at Charles's table also left their half finished drinks and reluctantly followed him to the main dining saloon. None of them felt at all hungry now. The devastating news of the sinking of the 'Sheffield', and the manner it had been accomplished had taken away most of their appetites.

H. M. S. Sheffield. The fearsome destruction of a ship by an Exocet.
The attack knocked out all her fire fighting ability

From that day onwards the tone of the voyage altered. Since the sinking of the 'Sheffield' it was all so different, something out of the ordinary, something they had never experienced before in their lives, the prospect that they could die a violent death. The activity with regard to emergency drills and various other safety requirements were increased and tightened up. It

seemed to Charles that each time he came off watch there was always some
thing or other extra to be done or remembered, or some new piece of
equipment issued that had to be carried by him at all times for the safety of
the ship and crew should they be damaged in any way from an attack by an
Exocet.

As the 'Conveyor' continued to sail southward amidst an increasing aura of
apprehension and not a little fear, Charles soon realised the seriousness of
their situation, and that they were sailing into a battle zone totally bereft of
any kind of defence against an attack. "Just as the Chief said," he muttered
to himself. "Bloody sitting ducks." The seriousness of the situation was
brought home even more to Charles when orders were issued to discontinue
the use of the standard Merchant Navy lifejackets, and all personnel on board
were issued with the self-inflatable Royal Navy lifejackets, followed by
flash masks, gauntlets and orange rubber survival suits. Later, the engine
room staff and anyone who worked below decks were issued with anti-gas
respirators. This particular piece of survival equipment was an afterthought,
as news had come through that choking fumes inside the 'Sheffield' after she
had been hit had contributed to many of the casualties. All this paraphernalia
had to be slung round the waist before going anywhere. To Charles it was
really irksome to have to carry all this equipment about himself, but he fully
appreciated the necessity of all these safety precautions.

Charles's foreboding of what might lie ahead increased immeasurably when
orders were given that all the crew had to give a blood test to ascertain their
blood group, should they need a blood transfusion in the event of any of them
being wounded. He was informed that this was standard practice for all
personnel going into action. Also, all the crew were issued with field
dressings. This last item, and all the ominous implications it held, was
viewed with grave misgivings by Charles. It was also alleged that the
Argentinean troops were suffering from an epidemic of Typhus on the
Falklands, and all hands on board had to be duly inoculated against this most
virulent of diseases. No-one enjoys inoculations and this only added to their
misery.

There were many emergency drills now, some purely for exercise and some
for real. Charles accepted all these interruptions to his daily routine in his
usual stoical manner, but at times he was sorely tried, especially when the
alarm siren blared out at three in the morning. Charles's emergency station

was in the engine control room monitoring all the important functions in the engine room to keep the 'Conveyor' moving. He also had to start up all the fire pumps in readiness for immediate use. Having been rudely awakened and dragged out of his bunk at three in the morning to race down to the engine room, the adrenaline pumping furiously through his veins, only to find it was an exercise, pushed Charles's equanimity to the limit. On the other hand, he was always greatly relieved when he found out it was only an exercise. On one occasion, and much to Charles's and others amusement, a submarine alert was activated and every one rushed to their emergency stations only to find out it was a school of whales that threw everyone into a panic.

It was a lovely warm evening with the 'Conveyor' ploughing steadily through a flat calm sea, Charles and a few of his fellow officers were taking a leisurely constitutional around the deck just before dinner. They had passed a number of military personnel during their stroll and courteously exchanged a 'good evening' with them. They continued with their constitutional pleasantly chatting away when Charles suddenly spoke out.

"Hey you guys, have you noticed anything different with those military blokes?"

His companions looked a trifle puzzled. "No, what?"

"Well all of them have been issued with identity tags to hang round their necks," Charles said.

"You are dead right Charles, now you mention it I do remember seeing those 'dog tags' around their necks, and we Merchant Navy wallahs have got sod all identification," remarked one of the group.

"And I bet we won't be getting any either," added Charles. "What I am going to do is to wrap up my Merchant Navy identity card along with my bankers card and my cheque book in a polythene waterproof wrapper and cram them into my gas mask case underneath my gas mask. We always have to carry it around with us so it will be always on our person. It would be wise for you all to do the same," suggested Charles.

"Good thinking Charles," they chorused.

"And another thing. In the event of the unthinkable happening and we do get sunk, it would be wise to cram a woolly sweater into your gas mask case. I think there should be room. It could be bloody cold down in the South Atlantic," warned Charles.

They all nodded in agreement. It was to prove a most judicious precaution.

A further ominous happening occurred as they steamed southward. Every day at precisely 3pm an Argentinean Boeing 707 flew over the armada, taking photographs and obviously plotting their position. Charles knew that the Navy kept one Sea Harrier permanently on stand by, fully armed and ready to take off to bring the Argentinean intruder down when the order was given. The Sea Harrier was on 15 minutes to scramble. It was always announced over the public address system and every day the pilot went to scramble, except one day the time to scramble came down as low as five minutes.

Charles walked into the officer's lounge just in time to hear a young naval officer telling the assembled company that before the pilot could have permission to take off and intercept the spy plane, the Navy had to have confirmation from Mrs. Thatcher and her war cabinet.

"What?" a stunned voice exclaimed. "What was that you just said?"

"I said," replied the young naval officer in a sort of bored voice, "we have to have permission from Mrs.T. and her war cabinet before we can do anything about that Argie reconnaissance plane."

"Jesus Christ, do we have to get her permission to go for a crap as well?"

They all burst into laughter at this remonstration. The slightly embarrassed young Naval officer replied somewhat hesitantly, "Well no, of course not, but you must remember that any Prime Minister and their war cabinets are very touchy on these points of starting hostilities between nations. They always are."

This explanation failed to pacify Charles. "Touchy, touchy," repeated Charles. "How bloody touchy will it be if one of those bastards Exocets touches us? Will Maggie tell the Argies not to fire at us because she would not let us fire on their plane?"Charles was always recognised as a very placid person, slow to anger, always thought things through before making any kind of controversial statement or move, but the tension of the whole situation was building up inside everyone on board, even in Charles, as every day by every hour they steamed nearer and nearer to the battle zone, knowing not what may happen to them. This atmosphere took its toll on everybody's temperament.

"What a bloody way to run a war," Charles concluded his outburst. He spun round and stormed out of the lounge leaving its occupants quite taken aback. They had never seen Charles in a rage like this before and what he had said had given them plenty to think about, and it showed on all their faces.

The weather was still very humid and unpleasantly warm and the work had become very strenuous, but Charles threw himself into his work in the engine room. The harder he worked the better it was for him, for in some way it would take his mind off what the forthcoming days could hold for him. One morning, while Charles was on watch, all hell broke loose down in the engine room. There were two main turbo alternators, one of which was on full load providing all the ships electrical power, the second alternator was the back up if anything went wrong with number one. A pipe that carried sea water to cool the electrical end of the main alternator burst, and sea water under great pressure began spraying everywhere. Charles immediately realised what a dangerous situation they were in. If the sea water came into contact with anything electrical on the generator board it would cause a complete shut down of everything electrical on board the ship. The steering mechanism was all electrical, and should that shut down the 'Conveyor' would be out of control, and a rogue vessel steaming at 16 knots in a convoy is no joke. Charles responded to this emergency at once, calling on his assistant, Bill, they went to the back up generator and managed to get it going, thus averting the danger of a total shut down while the other engineers repaired the broken pipe.

A very concerned, and not a little frightened Wing Commander, who had been seconded to the engine room had watched all these events, and when normal service had been resumed he looked at the sweating and grime covering Charles and his fellow engineers and shook his head. "I do not know how the hell you fellows can work in a place like this all the time, it would drive me insane. I would not work down here for a million pounds," he remarked in total awe of what he had seen, as they quickly got the emergency under control.

Charles smiled, wiping his oil covered hands on a piece of 'waste'. "It's all in a day's work and it's what you get used to," Charles said without a hint of any boastfulness. "And what you just said, coming from a man who, without thinking or hesitation, would climb into the cockpit of a plane and take off, not knowing what to expect to meet or whether you would return or not, we take as a great compliment. And I can tell you this, we seldom get any compliments at all down here."

"You damn well deserve them," replied the Wing Commander.

That small compliment to Charles and the engineers did wonders for their flagging morale.

Eventually the weather began to get cooler, and the humidity bearable in the engine room as they continued southwards towards the Falklands. Charles could not get out of his mind his concern about the lack of any armament to protect the 'Conveyor' from any kind of attack and he frequently expressed his fears to all and sundry at every opportunity.

Charles was pleasantly surprised whilst reading a book in his cabin during his off watch period when a knock on the door announced the entrance of the Chief.

"Hi Charles, got a spare beer?" he asked.

"Sure have, I was just going to break into one myself," replied Charles.

"Great, I love your cold lager," the Chief said with the emphasis on the word cold, and a knowing look on his face.

Charles laughed. "Can't beat cold ale, Chief, no matter how you get it."

"You are right Charles. Listen," he continued, "I want you to do me a favour, and give the day work engineer a hand to make machine gun mountings to be fitted to each wing of the bridge during your off watch periods."

The Chief knew Charles would not refuse to give up his off watch rest time, it was not his nature, it never was, and he knew of Charles's constant concern of the ship's total lack of fire power against any form of attack.

The Deadly Exocet
The most feared weapon in the Argentine armoury

"Sure will," Charles readily replied. "I suppose this is the beginning of arming up the ship after what happened to the 'Sheffield', is it Chief?"

"Don't hold your breath on that one Charles, as far as I hear or know this is all the armament we're going to bloody well get," he testily replied. "I will tell you something now Charles, just between you and me. I can't vouch for its authenticity, but I was told by one of the senior naval bods that the MoD turned down the request from the owners of the 'Conveyor' to fit mortars on both sides of the ship for firing 'Chaff' rockets; the bastards said it was too expensive.

"What in the hell is 'Chaff'?" a puzzled Charles asked.

"Well, as far as I can gather from the bits of info I have heard, it's an update on the last war's 'Snow System' used by the RAF during the bombing raids over Germany to confuse their radar. Apparently, when one of these rockets is launched, they explode or 'bloom' into a cloud of aluminium fragments which confuses the radar in one of those Exocet things, and puts them off their intended target."

"An intended target as big and important as us no doubt," retorted Charles angrily. "What would it have cost, Chief, to have a couple of these mortars fitted to the ship?"

"A measly six hundred quid each I believe. Can you understand those desk bound civil servants reasoning? Here we are carrying about ten million quid's worth of vitally important war equipment to win a war, and those bastards won't open their purse strings for six hundred quid."

"Civil servants have no brains in their heads - they are sitting on them all," Charles bitterly said.

They both sighed heavily and finished their beer in silence. Their morale had taken another massive blow.

The 'Chaff' Launcher
Had these been fitted to the 'Atlantic Conveyor' she might have been saved.

Weapons Of Air Warfare

R. A. F. Harriers G. R. 3s carried by the 'Atlantic Conveyor'

R. A. F. Chinook Helicopter

8

RENDEZVOUS WITH
THE TASK FORCE

On May 18th, in reasonably calm weather, although dull and overcast, the Assault Group rendezvoused with the original Task Force. The 'Conveyor' was positioned to sail between the two aircraft carriers, 'HMS Hermes' and 'HMS Invincible'; that being the most practicable position to be in for transferring the implements of war to these sinister looking aircraft carriers. In the engine room, Charles was kept very busy with constant speed adjustments in order to keep station with the two carriers, whilst the Harriers were wheeled out one by one to the forward flight deck and flew off safely to whichever of the carriers they had been allotted. Some of the helicopters, including another Chinook, also departed to a designated carrier.

At every opportunity Charles would always come on deck to watch any activities, especially any air manoeuvres. It completely fascinated him, the precision and timing of the aircraft movements lifting off and landing. Unfortunately, on this occasion he was too fully occupied in the engine room to have time to come up on deck and witness his favourite manoeuvres. It irked him just a tad. At the end of his watch Charles came on deck. The last of the Harriers had flown away, but the sight of the two carriers steaming on both sides of the 'Conveyor' really impressed him. To him it was a magnificent sight.

When all the transferring of aircraft had been completed, and the innumerable 'vertrepping' of food and stores also completed, the 'Conveyor' and the rest of the Assault Group steamed away to the eastward. What neither Charles nor any other person on the 'Conveyor', or any one else in the Assault Group knew, was that 'HMS Invincible' had serious engine trouble in one of her main propeller shafts, forcing her speed to be so reduced as to render her unable to launch any aircraft, and effectively putting her out of participating in any hostile action. Had the Argentineans known this, they would have had a whole different strategy to the forthcoming conflict.

One of the naval officers passed by Charles as he stood watching all that was going on around him. "What's happening now?" enquired Charles. "We have changed course and we are steaming eastward."

"Yes, old chap. We are heading eastwards to get out of range of the Argie air force that are based on the mainland," replied the young officer.

This bit of information brought a certain amount of comfort to Charles's troubled mind. However, there followed a very frustrating period of days for Charles. Firstly, to his dismay, they were still over-flown by enemy aircraft on a number of occasions, and the shrill sirens of the emergency alerts still continued to blight the rest periods of everyone on board.

On one of these emergency alerts the 'Conveyor' was taking on oil fuel from a fleet tanker as they steamed along, and Charles, with his engine room crew, had to do an emergency break away which could be fraught with danger. Thankfully they had all been well trained to perform this duty during the passage down to the Falklands, and everything went off without a hitch, much to Charles's relief. Secondly, the frustration was compounded by the numerous rumours that were rife amongst the ship's company. It was difficult to tell what was the truth and what was just a figment of someone's imagination, and all these things only added to the tension that was being felt throughout the 'Conveyor'. On most days Captain North came into the control room and chatted away with the engineers about something or other, even though it might have been just to pass the time of day away, and he did the same in other departments of the ship in an attempt to relieve some of the tension building up inside everyone. The Navy, in their regular broadcasts every evening over the ships public address system, did their best to keep everyone well informed of the present situation on the Falklands, but even

The Task Force Troop Ship

'Canberra'
P. & O. luxury cruise liner in her pristine livery

'Canberra'
Anchored in San Carlos Bay. The luxury look had gone.

the Naval Captain had to admit that he was also suffering from the 'mushroom syndrome', explaining he was also being 'kept in the dark and fed bullshit'.

Charles was sitting in the officer's lounge having a quiet beer and wondering how Betty was faring alone at home listening to the broadcasts on the BBC, when a few other officers walked in.

"Hi Charles. Ready for another beer?" asked one of them.

"Sure, why not," he readily replied.

"Am I getting fed up with all these air raid warnings and bloody emergency drills? I thought we were supposed to be out of range of those bastards," grumbled a young officer.

"We never seem to get into our bunks for a good kip, just catnapping when ever it is possible," rejoined another. They all nodded in agreement.

Charles sensed an air of despondency amongst some of the junior officers, and he decided to try and lift this gloom with some news he had just heard. "Did you lot hear on the broadcast that the SAS had raided Pebble Island, killing quite a few of the Argie invading force?" Charles revealed.

"No we didn't. Did they do any other damage?" they asked.

"Yes, they destroyed a number of 'Pucara' aircraft as well," answered Charles.

"What in hell's name is a "Pucara" aircraft?" they chorused.

"It's a sort of light bomber," Charles said knowingly.

"Great, that's a few less of those Argie bastards to have a go at us."

They were all extremely aware of the lack of defences on the ship from an attack from the air, and they seemed to gain a certain amount of satisfaction from the news Charles imparted to them, which was just what Charles had hoped it would do.

Port San Carlos 'Atlantic Conveyor' Destination.

Sunset May 25th. Before the fatal Exocet attack

The weather had become very cold and the sea was a grey turbulent mass with cresting white waves. Charles was asleep when the alarm sounded, but this was not an air raid. The 'Conveyor' was ordered to take part in a search for 19 men from the SAS whose helicopter had ditched into the icy sea, and Charles went into the control room to see if he could be of any assistance in the manoeuvring of the engines. After nearly six hours of searching, none of the SAS men were found and the search was abandoned. This saddened Charles immensely, although in his heart he knew the men would have had little chance of survival in those sea conditions. Only yesterday morning he had taken the sea water temperature as part of his watch duties, and it was 2° C.

'Poor buggers,' he said to himself. "What a way to go; and we will go the same way if we get hit and dumped into the sea," he reflected.

One of those missing was the naval helicopter pilot that Charles had got to know slightly over a beer or two. Charles had the greatest admiration for the helicopter pilots and the fantastic job they did, and with the expertise with which they executed their duties under the sometimes hazardous weather conditions. He remembered the night the ship was pitching violently and rolling heavily, her bow dipping into the waves and shipping them green over the foredeck. The pilot of a Wessex 1V was hovering over the foredeck taking on board men and materials. At one point the helicopter was completely enveloped in spray, yet oblivious to his own safety and with expert handling of his helicopter, continued hovering, keeping in position, until all the men were safely winched up into the helicopter.

The rumours continued to persist: they were going into the Falklands Sound tomorrow, then they were not. It began to tell on the nerves of everyone and tempers became very short, but a little relief to this stress came by way of mail from home. Charles was pleased, and not a little surprised, to receive any mail at all. Here he was at sea, miles from home and in a wartime situation. He could hardly believe his eyes, to see letters lying on his desk when he came off duty. He hastily ripped open the letters and avidly read every word in them over and over again before he even took a shower and cleaned himself up from his engine room duties. He was overjoyed to read about what was going on at home, and to remind him that there were more peaceful things going on in this mad, mad world. Betty was a wonderful letter writer, always full of local information, always interesting, and above all, always telling him how much she loved him and missed him, and to look after himself. Whenever he read Betty's letters it was if she was actually in his cabin talking to him.

He discovered later how the mail arrived on the 'Conveyor'. It had been flown out from the UK to the Ascension Islands, and a Nimrod aircraft would bring it out to the Task Force. The special floatation mail bags were dropped into the sea for the duty diver on whichever naval ship was nearest to them to swim out and retrieve them. This was apparently a standard naval procedure for delivering non-essential mail. Charles found himself writing letters home every day. The more dangerous the situation became, the more air raid warnings he had to endure, the more he found sanctuary in communicating with Betty. He also wrote to his father, brother and sisters, and even relatives he would not normally write to. It was a sort of loneliness and homesickness, and a defined awareness of being in a situation which was very dangerous and from which he may not come out of unscathed. Charles was not alone in feeling this way. It permeated throughout all the departments on the 'Conveyor', judging by the numbers of letters posted on board every day.

9

ORDERED INTO
THE FALKLAND SOUND

Charles entered the officers lounge full of foreboding. He had found a brief message left on his writing desk when he had come off watch summoning him to attend a meeting there at 1300hrs. The lounge was full but no one was drinking, but most were fitfully smoking, occasionally a forced laugh would break over the low murmur of voices. Obviously everyone was as worried as Charles. The tension in the lounge he felt you could cut with a knife.

"Any idea what this all about?" asked Bill, his watch mate.

"Nope, just as much in the dark as you are. But I have a bloody good idea," replied Charles.

"What's that?" queried Bill.

Before Charles could answer, the lounge door opened and the Royal Naval Captain, Captain Layard, strode in and stood by the bar.

"Good afternoon gentlemen," he said. There was a quiet response from the anxiously waiting officers.

"I have this morning received from HQ a message stating that a landing will take place on the Falklands at San Carlos tomorrow, May 21st at dawn. My instructions are that we are to be ready to enter the Falkland Sound in company with the 'Elk' on 'D' Day + 2. Any questions gentlemen?" he asked.

The news was greeted by all in the lounge with a feeling of relief that the interminable waiting was over, but Charles still had his feeling of misgivings about whether the 'Conveyor' was going to be able to withstand any damage from an air attack.

"Yes sir," he said. "I have a question and I speak for all on board. It's a very important question too. What sort of protection will we have from aerial attacks when we go into the Sound? As you yourself know we have got sod all but a couple of peashooters on each side of the bridge."

"Good question," the Captain replied. "I can assure you that the 'Conveyor' will be protected by Frigates which will be stationed at each end of the Sound, and also by Rapier missiles which will have been set up along the top of the cliffs above where we will be offloading all our equipment to back up the landing. Does that answer your question satisfactorily?"

The Two Commanders
Captain Ian North and Captain Michael Layard. R. N.

Charles was not totally convinced. "You seem pretty bloody certain that these Rapier missiles will be in place when we get there."

"Let me once again assure you all, the military have made the installation of the Rapiers their first priority after the landing."

"What if they can't, and they are not in position?" Charles was not going to be put off by any glib answers.

"We will cross that bridge when we come to it," the Naval Captain retorted, obviously not being used to his assurances being questioned. "Any more questions?" He paused awhile looking around the room. "No. Right then, I will keep you informed on all the up to date situations. That's all gentlemen." He walked quickly out of the lounge.

The assembled company in the lounge remained quiet, taking everything in that had been said until someone spoke up. "I think its time for a beer, don't you?" As of one man they all agreed and it took some of the tension out of the meeting.

"You certainly put that Captain on the spot Charles," said the Chief.

"Yes, but we still are no better off knowing if we will have enough protection from an Argie air attack," he grumbled.

"Well Charles, what's to be will be," answered the Chief with a deep sigh.

"I wish to hell I could be that philosophical," replied Charles, far from happy with his lot.

On May 21st, all on board the 'Conveyor' heard the news that a landing had been made at San Carlos and that they had successfully established the required beach head. The landings had taken place unimpeded. This was wonderful news to Charles. It really heartened him and made him feel that by the time they arrived at San Carlos the war as such would be over, and it would be just a matter of going into San Carlos, unopposed, discharging all their cargo and sailing out again, hopefully for the UK.

This aura of hopefulness of an early and safe return home was soon to be shattered. The lack of opposition by the Argentinean occupying forces to the landing forces was only a brief respite; later in the day a news bulletin announced that the Argentinean Air Force had launched a sustained attack on the naval ships in the San Carlos waters, and 'HMS Ardent' had been hit and severely damaged with the deaths of 24 men. The damage was of such a nature that the order had been given to abandon ship. 'HMS Antelope' had also been hit and was dead in the water, but her guns were still active and she was continuing firing, being used as a gun platform.

"So much for the protection of the Rapier missiles we were so confidently assured by the Navy would be in position to protect all ships in the Sound," snorted Charles to the Chief as they worked down in the engine room. "I bloody well knew it was all bullshit." complained Charles.

"Aye, you're right," replied the Chief. "And I don't suppose we will be getting any long-winded explanation from the Navy why the missiles, if they were in position, didn't shoot the Argie bastards down before they could get to our ships."

"It's the old 'mushroom syndrome' beloved of the MoD kicking in again," groaned Charles.

"What about the two frigates that were hit? Were they the ones stationed at each end of the Sound, supposedly to protect us from any air attacks?" a very worried Chief asked.

"God only knows," Charles fervently replied.

'D' Day + 2 arrived, the day scheduled for the 'Conveyor' to move into the Sound, but no orders came for her to proceed. The Canberra', 'Norland' and their companion ship 'Europic Ferry' had all gone into San Carlos with the troops on' 'D Day, and had returned unscathed to the Task Force at sea. This gave some comfort and hope to Charles that the 'Conveyor' would do the same. Nevertheless, the sinking of 'HMS Ardent' and the disablement of 'HMS Antelope' only served to heighten Charles's fear and premonition that the 'Conveyor' would be a sitting duck should the Argentineans launch an attack on them from the air.

The air attack alerts continued, and even intensified, so that Charles found it impossible to get more than a few hours sleep at a time. It was beginning to

The Task Force protection Vessels
at the Falklands Sound

H. M. S. Ardent
Hit by 15 missiles. Sank May 21st
22 killed

H. M. S. Coventry
Hit by Exocet missile. Sank May 25th
17 killed

wear him down. They steamed further to the eastward to take on more bunker fuel from one of the RFA (Royal Fleet Auxiliary) fleet tankers, and true to form, during the refuelling an air attack alert was sounded and an emergency breakaway had to be accomplished. These breakaways were accomplished much more easily, as a special quick shut off valve in the fuel hose had been fitted by the Navy engineers for just such an eventuality, a few days before they arrived into the war zone.

Charles and Bill were having a tea break from working in the engine room. "I am beginning to see my arse with these naval blokes who keep on telling us we are out of range of enemy planes," moaned Charles.

"You are not the only one," Bill replied quickly. They are over head every day no matter how far we steam to the east."

"You heard 'HMS Antelope' blew up?" "Yes, and I heard on the grapevine, or from the bullshit bucket, take your pick, we are going into the Sound tomorrow," Bill announced. "I will believe that when we get there. It's getting like Argentina or any other Latin American country: manâna, manâna," he scoffed.

On May 25th, there was a great apprehension over all the ship because this day was the most important in the calendar of the Argentineans history. It was their national day and they had named it "Viente Cinco Mayo". Charles felt that if the Argentineans were preparing to do anything spectacular against them to boost the flagging moral of their troops and their people in Argentina, this was to be the day. It was a feeling that was shared by all on board the 'Conveyor'.

Definite orders came that morning for the 'Conveyor' to be prepared to go into the Falklands Sound that afternoon, and to adjust course and speed to arrive just before nightfall. To Charles that morning and the early part of the afternoon were a complete nightmare. On an average they suffered about one emergency alert an hour. The news of the sinking of the two HM ships by the Argentina Air Force, the inadequacy of their own anti-aircraft defence, and the fact they were now going hell for leather for the centre of the war zone, the Sound, placed an unbearable strain on Charles, he constantly feared the worst that could happen and he could see no way the 'Conveyor' could avoid it.

10

THE EXOCET ATTACK

Charles came off watch at 1400hrs that afternoon. His hours of duty during the day had been changed to 1000hrs to 1400hrs, and at night 2200hrs to 0400hrs. This extra time during the night was in order to have two senior engineers in the engine room at all times. They had not altered the clocks to coincide with the time zones as they sailed from the UK. The whole Task Force stayed on what the Navy euphemistically called Zulu time. Charles knew it as GMT, Greenwich Mean Time, but copying the Navy, euphemistically he called it General Margaret Thatcher time, much to the amusement of all the engine room staff. Because of not altering the time zones they had to alter the working day to coincide with the daylight hours which were approximately 1000hrs to 1930hrs.

From the very moment Charles was told the news that they would be going into the war-torn Falkland Sound, Port Carlos to be exact, his thoughts of Betty became uppermost in his mind. The situation in the Sound which was promised by the young Naval Officer, airily dismissing their concerns over the dangers of sending in an unarmed Merchant ship laden with vital and valuable war material; that there would be a frigate stationed at each end of the Sound to protect them from any attack, had all gone 'pear shaped'. Those frigates had now been hit and sunk, and Charles wondered if the promised Rapier missiles were in place ashore, and if the whole plan for their protection was in disarray.

<u>The Argentine Front Line Strike Force</u>

France supplied super Etendards of the second naval attack force.
They were armed with the fearsome 'Exocets' that sank the
'Atlantic Conveyor'

Argentine A-4 Sky Hawks. They were armed with guided bombs.

He snatched a quick lunch, and as there had been no emergency alerts for two hours decided a quick nap would be the most beneficial thing for him to do. He really was mentally and physically weary. He had no sooner laid down on the top of his bunk, fully dressed in readiness for any alert that might sound, when the emergency alert klaxon blared out and he rushed down to his station in the engine room. This one was serious, for the first time the emergency went to Red, which was maximum awareness. They waited anxiously and silently. Not a soul spoke. After what seemed to be an interminable time the emergency went to yellow, and then green. The apparent danger had passed. Charles breathed a big sigh of relief and there were smiles all round as they stood down.

Charles wearily climbed up the engine room ladders and made his way to his cabin. He lay down once again on his bunk and eventually fell asleep absolutely exhausted. Some time later he suddenly awoke to an awareness that something was not quite right. He swung his long legs over the side of his bunk and sat for awhile, listening and wondering what had made him wake so suddenly. He shook his head in puzzlement, slid off his bunk and went to go to his bathroom. At that very moment the klaxon once again commenced blaring out an emergency, and over the public address system came the urgent warning.

"Action stations! Action stations! Red alert! Red alert! Enemy air attack imminent."

Charles's heart missed a beat and then went into overdrive. Instead of going to the bathroom, which he sorely needed to do, he reached for his lifejacket and hastily started pulling it over his head, when the public address system screeched frantically.

"Hit the deck! Hit the deck!"

Before Charles could throw himself on to the deck, there was one almighty explosion. The whole of the 'Conveyor' shuddered and Charles was thrown flat on his face on to the cabin deck. His bunk, on which he had only moments before been asleep, moved towards him so that the carpet he was lying on rucked up and prevented it from toppling on top of him. His heavy desk which was mounted on the forward bulkhead fortunately slewed away from him into the far corner of his cabin.

Charles felt something hit him in the small of the back, but at first he could not make out what it was because all the lights had gone out. Then the emergency standby generators kicked in and restored the lights, and he was able to make out that it was the deck head light shade which had dropped down from above and hit him. All the things that were crashing around in his cabin missed him, except a bucket containing his dirty washing soaking in water and washing powder. It had somehow found its way from the bathroom and hit him hard on his side spilling all its contents over him. He let out a string of curses. Among this mayhem Charles realised all his worst fears and foreboding had become a reality. The 'Conveyor', without any adequate defences to repel an air attack, had been struck and severely damaged by God knows what.

Charles sensed that the 'Conveyor' was now lying dead in the water, and more frighteningly, she was on fire, and with all that high octane fuel stored on board for the aircraft and inside the helicopter's tanks, he momentarily panicked thinking they were all going to go up in one huge fireball. His natural tendency, throughout his life, to remain calm and lucid in any circumstances soon took over. All the endless emergency drills and lectures he had been subjected to, much to his and everyone's displeasure, on how to react in such a situation as this clearly came back to his mind, and he inwardly thanked himself that he had listened so intently to those instructions, for they now stood between him and death.

Charles's immediate thought was to get out of his cabin which was rapidly filling with acrid smoke, and get to his emergency station in the engine room as quickly as possible. He snatched his anti-flash gear and gas mask that he always hung on the bulkhead next to the door, and took hold of the door handle to open the door, but it would not move an inch. He took a firmer grip of the door handle with both hands and gave one almighty heave, but the door remained tightly closed. A sudden flash of panic swept over him again when he realised that the explosion, and the subsequent listing of the ship, had warped the door frame, jamming the door solidly shut. Charles instinctively knew what to do. He stood back from the door and launched his 14 stone frame at the door, but it stayed firmly closed. Fear gave him extra strength and he threw himself a second time at the door. A searing pain shot through his shoulders, but the door gave way slightly. Ignoring the pain he hit the door a third time and it tore off its hinges.

Charles dropped on all fours and crawled through the open door into the alleyway. The alleyway was filling up with suffocating black smoke and getting darker by the minute as more acrid smoke poured in. He shakily stood up and was surprised to find he was sweating profusely. He could feel his heart pounding away like a trip hammer. He started to struggle into his anti-flash gear and gas mask when suddenly the public address system screeched into sound again. "Red alert! Red alert! Hit the deck! Hit the deck!" Charles did not need a second warning. He threw himself face down on the alleyway deck and covered the back of his head with his hands, just as another mighty explosion ripped through the ship. The 'Conveyor' shuddered alarmingly and heeled further over to starboard and an eerie

'Atlantic Conveyor' engine control room looking aft,
steel door at the very end led to the annex.

silence descended. After a few minutes Charles stood up again trembling just a little. From what he could see in the alleyway that had become noticeably darker because it was now completely filled with dense smoke, there was no one else in the alleyway. He made sure his gas mask was properly on, and by sheer instinct groped his way along the smoke-filled alleyway towards the engine room control room which was his emergency station.

Charles's cabin was situated on the fourth deck and he had to descend three more decks through the smoke and increasing heat to reach the main deck level, and then enter the engine room. On his way down he encountered a number of people at third deck level where the officers' lounge was situated. The lounge had been designated as one of the main mustering points for emergency stations. Charles had no time to ask anyone what had happened, such was his haste to reach his own emergency station, but what did catch his eye was that all the people at that emergency point had already donned their survival suits as if preparing to abandon ship. Although he had no time to ponder why they were so dressed, it did worry him and made him wonder just how badly the 'Conveyor' had been damaged.

When Charles arrived in the engine room, at the control room door there was little smoke in evidence. He removed his gas mask from his heavily perspiring red face, caused by his exertions to get to the engine room as fast as humanly possible and the restricted flow of air brought about by wearing the gas mask. He left his gas mask hanging by its straps around his neck, knowing full well that he was going to need it again, and no doubt very quickly. He opened the control room door and he was immediately taken aback by the complete shambles that met his gaze. The control room was a long narrow room situated in a forward to aft direction. The main electrical switchboard, the six individual panels containing the boiler control and main engine control, the main engine revolution counters, the oil fuel, ballasting and bilge panels were all situated in this long narrow room and each panel had many various gauges of different shapes and sizes. The shock of the explosion had shattered the glass in all these gauges so that there was broken glass everywhere underfoot. The whole of the control room was an utter disaster.
Most of the Engineers and Mechanics were already in the control room.

"What the hell is going on here?" Charles shouted to no one in particular.

Fire Pump Room

"We're trying to engage the breakers for the two emergency diesel generators," a hysterical voice called back. Charles could see that the ship's main turbine engines had stopped completely and the fires in the boilers had gone out, so that the steam pressure was decreasing. The engine room was in a desperate condition. Through all this mayhem Charles spotted the Chief Engineer on the engine room telephone.

"What's the problem Chief?" he said rather anxiously.

"I am trying to establish contact with the bridge to see what's going on, and let them know the situation down here, but the bridge phone is out of action, and would you believe it, the bloody emergency battery operated telephone is buggered as well," the Chief replied testily.

"What the hell caused the explosion?"

"I really do not know, but I am aware we have been hit by something pretty big."

Starter Panel

"Do you think we have been bombed or hit by one of these Exocet things?"

"As I said Charles, I have no idea, but whatever it was that hit us packed one hell of a punch. It needed to to bring the 'Conveyor' to a dead stop."

The Chief turned around and addressed everyone in the engine room in his usual calm and commanding manner.

"OK, enough of this talking. Let's get to work and try and straighten out this mess down here, and get the emergency generators going."

11

FIGHTING TO KEEP AFLOAT

Every one in the engine room knew that they were facing an enormous task to save the ship, no more so than Charles. It was now a race against time to keep the Conveyor afloat. They still did not know what had struck them but they instinctively knew the ship had been delivered a mortal blow. Their main priority now was to make sure that all the emergency equipment was running, and to keep it running to give as much assistance to those on deck and on the bridge on whom they relied so much in their efforts to save the ship. Under the command of the Chief, who was showing great powers of leadership, the engine room staff set about their various tasks with a commendable calmness that belied the fear that was contained within them.

At last the emergency diesels were started up and engaged to the switchboard, the very heart beat of the ship. "Charles, go and try to get to the fire pump remote control panel, and get that pump running at full speed if you can. We are going to need all the sea water we can get to fight these fires on board." ordered the Chief.

"On my way Chief."

The Conveyor had been fitted with two fire pumps, but the one in the engine room was out of action and irreparable. The other pump was situated in one of the stabiliser compartments. Without any thought for his own safety, Charles moved off towards the after end of the control room where the starter panel was housed. The smoke in the control room was gradually increasing and it became necessary for Charles to wear his gas mask again. Arriving at the fire pump panel, he immediately turned the starter switch on and a red light appeared on the panel, indicating that the pump was running, Charles let out a deep breath of relief he had been holding inside him.

"Thank God for that," he said to himself as he watched the pressure gauge on the panel very intently, awaiting a rise in pressure. After what seemed an eternity the needle slowly moved around the gauge to maximum pressure.

Charles prayed that the pressure would remain steady as it was vital to the fighting of the fires on board. He stood back from the panel and looked around his immediate surroundings as best he could through his gas mask window, and concluded that the damage at this end of the control room did not seem so bad considering the chaos elsewhere in the control room. He thought it was a miracle that this place worked at all. Charles turned to return to the main control room, when he suddenly heard a plaintive cry, "Help me, oh help me," that stopped him in his tracks. It appeared to be coming from behind a doorway which was about thirty feet to his right and led into a small room called the annexe.

Charles moved swiftly towards the steel annexe door and took hold of the brass ring handle, which to his surprise was very hot. He turned the brass ring and the door swung open. Charles was immediately engulfed in thick smoke and a blast of heat hit him. He dropped onto his hands and knees and crawled down the three steps into the annexe keeping beneath the worst of the heat. He paused for awhile to get his bearings in the smoke filled room, when he heard the agonising cry again. "Help me, help me." Guided by this pleading voice, he crawled to his left desperately trying to find the source of the cry. The cry for help ceased, and a few minutes later Charles encountered a body that he recognised as the four to eight watchkeeping mechanic, Ernie Vickers.

The body was trapped across the threshold of a steel door holding the door open. Charles could not tell what injuries Ernie had sustained. He could see very little through his gas mask facia into the murky atmosphere. Charles was beginning to feel the effects of the smoke and the intense heat, his gas mask was not coping too well with the smoke. He reached the lifeless body of Ernie and tried to lift him by the shoulders and drag him through the door, but Ernie was a tall and very heavy man, and with the smoke and heat affecting Charles more and more he was unable to move him. He quickly realised he must get help. He crawled back to the annexe door, his ears beginning to hurt with the heat, even though they were protected by his anti-flash helmet.

Charles arrived back into the control room with the utmost difficulty, his breathing heavily laboured. His exertions had completely exhausted him. "Chief, Ernie Vickers the mechanic is trapped in a steel doorway in the control annexe, and he looks pretty badly injured," he gasped out. "I need a breathing apparatus and someone to help me to get him out. I tried but he is too heavy for me on my own."

"No way Charles," the Chief firmly replied. "We have orders to evacuate the control room immediately. The heat and the smoke is making our presence untenable. We have got to get out of here."

The smoke was now quite dense, and having no breathing apparatus to hand they had no alternative but to leave the control room as quickly as possible. They passed through the centre door of the control room between the boilers and up the steel ladders to the main deck where the safety room was situated. As part of the emergency drills, parties were set up at various points about the ship, fully kitted up with all the accoutrements for the express purpose of rescuing people from smoke filled areas. Such a party was in readiness in the safety room when the engine room contingent arrived.

The Chief explained the situation in the control annexe to the rescue party, and then to everyone's astonishment he spoke out. "OK, before any of you lot attempt a rescue and put yourself into danger, I feel it is my duty as Chief to go back down to the annexe to see the conditions and if it is possible to get Ernie out. It is no good sending a party down there and finding it impossible to rescue him, and yourselves getting trapped down there and not be able to get back. If that happened, for the rest of my life I would feel responsible for your deaths."

Although still exhausted Charles interrupted. "Not on your own, you won't be going anywhere. I will go with you to help you find your way and I will not take any orders to stay behind, and that is final."

The Chief gave Charles a long hard look. He knew well enough it would be useless arguing with Charles, having sailed with him before, and time was precious if an attempt to get Ernie out was to succeed.

"Are you fit enough?" he asked.

"I am fit enough," Charles quickly replied.

"OK let's go then."

Still wearing only their gas masks, they returned to the control room and groped their way to the annexe door. There was some smoke but they did not think it was too bad to make a rescue, and the heat was just about bearable even without being suitably clad in rescue equipment. The Chief opened the annexe door and they both looked in. They could see well enough through the smoke to assess the condition of the annexe room and test the temperature. They looked at each other and nodded as a sign they both thought it was tenable for the rescue party to enter and attempt to save the trapped mechanic. They quickly turned and retraced their steps back to the safety room on the main deck.

Charles went ahead of the Chief and was half way up the engine room ladder when he sensed that the Chief was not right behind him. He turned around but not could see him through the smoke. His heart missed a beat.

"Dear God. Has he tripped and fallen somewhere?" Charles said to himself, and he immediately went back down into the engine room. He had hardly gone a quarter of the way back when to his great relief the Chief appeared out of the gloom. Charles grabbed the Chief by the arm and they returned together to the safety room. Charles ripped off his gas mask and turning to the Chief exclaimed.

"Where the hell did you get to down there?"

The Chief was taken aback by the abruptness of Charles's question.

"I just went on top of the boilers to see how much steam pressure was left," he replied, as though it was the most natural thing in the world to do.

"You did what?" yelled Charles.

"I went on top of the boilers to check the steam pressure," the Chief repeated.

Charles shook his head in amazement. "You scared the shit out of me when I realised you weren't right behind me. I thought you had fallen and was a goner in all that heat and smoke."

"Sorry about that Charles," the Chief said, a little embarrassed at having caused his good friend so much concern. "I was OK, but thanks all the same for coming back to look for me. I really appreciate that."

"No problem Chief."

The Chief turned to the rescue party and quickly explained to them the conditions they would find in the control room annexe, and detailed Charles's friend Brian Williams, the other third engineer, and the Senior engine room mechanic, Frank Foulkes, who were already fitted up with the breathing apparatus, to go down and attempt to rescue the trapped mechanic. Charles was briefed by the Chief to watch that they returned safely. The rescue party had hardly gone five minutes when Brian Williams returned.

"We need the special fire gloves Chief, every thing down there is too bloody hot to touch, we can't even get hold of the annexe door handle to open the door."

"Get them the fire gloves someone and quickly," shouted the Chief. Tensions were running high - they knew that time was running out to save Ernie .They returned to the engine room only to reappear minutes later.

"What the hell now?" yelled the Chief, who was becoming increasingly exasperated by the minute with all these delays.

" The alarm has gone off on my oxygen bottle," replied Brian. "It must be nearly empty."

"Doesn't any bastard ever check these things?" a now raging Chief asked. They fitted the new oxygen bottle, and with a third man now joining the rescue party returned again to the heat and smoke of the engine room. They

The 'Atlantic Conveyor' crippled and on fire!

struggled bravely through the most horrendous conditions, and eventually reached the trapped mechanic, and were met with a sickening sight of a badly charred body hardly recognisable as Ernie Vickers. They realised it would be to no avail to attempt to release the body, sadly they abandoned all attempts at rescue and returned to the safety room to impart the bad news to the Chief.

The rescue party arrived back from the control room for the third and final time when a third large explosion was heard and the 'Conveyor' shuddered once again.

"We have been hit again," someone shouted. "What the hell was it?" He received no answer. All the people in the safety room instinctively knew that their situation was deteriorating rapidly with this explosion, and it became apparent that they were losing the battle to keep the 'Conveyor' afloat.

Whilst the attempted rescue bid was proceeding, Herculean efforts were being made to extinguish the fire that was raging on the main cargo deck, C deck. Everyone in the safety room now turned their attention to the emergency switchboard which was situated in the safety room to keep the breakers for the emergency generators engaged. At last the Chief had got the emergency telephone working briefly and was in contact with the bridge giving them an up to date state of the control room.

"Ask them what the hell all the explosions were and what the hell is happening on deck?" said a concerned Charles.

"Will do Charles," he spoke into the bridge phone " Engine control room to bridge what have we been hit with and what is your present situation on deck?" asked the anxious Chief.

The entire safety control party gathered around the Chief and stood staring silently at him as he listened intently to the messages relayed to him from the bridge. All the while he was listening he avoided eye contact with all those who had gathered around him preferring to stare down at the oily deck. From time to time the Chief spoke out aloud "Right, Right, got that" then suddenly he exclaimed loudly to everyone's surprise "Jesus Christ". They seldom heard, if ever, their Chief blaspheme unless under the greatest of stress or hearing any disturbing news. The Chief raised his eyes for a brief moment and looked upon the startled and smoked grimed faces of his anxious staff. "Right Sir thanks for all the info update, keep us informed of the situation if it deteriorates any further we will do all we can down here to help" and he hung the telephone back on its cradle. The Chief took a deep breath and gave a little nervous cough. He spoke quietly and firmly to avoid any undue stress or panic to his staff.

"The news is not good, I will give it to you straight from the shoulder, we have been hit by two of those Exocet things and they have set us on fire, the fire crews are having the greatest of difficulties containing it, the flames have now reached the cargo on "C" deck, you remember seeing all those tents and marquees being stowed in there at Plymouth? It's all stuff dry as tinder, well they have now all gone up in flames and the bridge wants us to activate the CO_2 system right away."

This was the first time anyone had been told what had hit the 'Conveyor' and crippled her so severely; they stood there frozen in a state of shock.

"Lets get to it then and set off the CO_2 systems" the Chief abruptly ordered clapping his hands to snap them out of their torpor.

The 'Conveyor' was fitted with smothering CO_2 inert gas to all compartments. The idea of this system is that it releases a large amount of carbon dioxide gas on to the fire and smothers it by starving it of its life-giving oxygen. All the levers for directing the gas to each compartment were situated in the safety room and were quickly operated.

"I am going aft into the CO_2 bottle storage room to check if all the bottles have actually discharged themselves" declared the Chief.

"Do you want me to go with you as a back up?" asked a worried Charles. "Thanks for asking but no thanks Charles I will do this on my own and besides I need you down here as my second in command to keep things going and to see that everything is in order."

"Right you are Chief but I will give you ten minutes to get back here and if you are not back by then I will come after you" said Charles in a voice that brooked no argument.

"Thanks again Charles I appreciate your concern but I cannot send anyone else to do this you know that" replied the Chief.

Not for a moment did the Chief consider his own safety, he was that sort of man, he knew the risks and dangers from more exploding gas bottles or the thousands of gallons of 'Avcat' going up in a ball of fire or the tons of ammunition exploding, even the risk of another air attack but he did not hesitate for a moment and quickly left the safety control room without another backward glance.

He arrived on deck and hurriedly walked aft, there was smoke everywhere. He passed a blazing helicopter on its launch pad and there was an acrid smell of burning rubber and canvass all about the ship. He reached the small trap door that led into the CO_2 bottle room, he opened it and descended into that compartment. When he had quickly satisfied himself that all the gas bottles had discharged themselves he returned to the safety control room. On his arrival into the control room he was met by a barrage of questions from all directions "What's the latest news of the set up on deck Chief?" "Did the CO_2 put the fires out?" "What do we do next?". Only Charles asked quietly "How are you Chief, you look a bit pale."

"I am OK Charles. Well the news is that all the CO_2 gas has been discharged but to no avail, there is one hell of a big hole in the side of the ship so large that it is impossible for the gas to have any smothering effect and the fire is still raging and getting out of control. What's more it is getting dangerously close to the 'Avcat' tanks."

"What in the hell do we do now?" someone asked.

"Pray" said the Chief with a little smile. He never lost his sense of humour no matter what the circumstances were.

He looked at their strained expressions, faces covered in sweat and grime. "First off I must report to the bridge what the situation is down here and the failure of the CO_2 system and let them decide what next we should do."

He turned towards the bridge telephone and took it off its hook and spun the bell handle, nothing happened, the telephone remained dead. "That's all we need" he snorted " no bloody contact with the bridge now, that's really buggered it."

The second officer Mr. Phillip Bailey, who was a member of the Engine Room emergency party spoke up "Chief I can partially solve our communications problem."

"How's that?" said the Chief hopefully,

"By the simple expedient of running between our control room up five or six decks to the bridge carrying any information from you Chief to the Captain and vice-versa". He said it so matter of factly as though it was an every day practice drill.

"That's great Phil, but do you realise the danger you are putting yourself into out there?" the Chief asked him. "Its no picnic on deck I can tell you, I've been there."

Phil just shrugged his shoulders as if to say 'So what, it's the only way we are going to make contact with the bridge."

"OK, Phil get going and let them know our position down here."

No sooner had the Second Officer cleared the safety control room than smaller explosions were heard somewhere below. "That's the bottled gas stored on B deck starting to detonate from all the heat" intoned Charles; he knew the situation was indeed worsening. He also noticed that crew members were already filing past the safety room dressed in survival gear and appeared to be heading for their life raft stations.

"Do you think we should be making tracks for our survival gear and get to our life raft stations Chief?" someone asked.

"Not yet we have to wait for the Second Officer to return with any orders."

They stood around, fidgeting, unsure of their safety, talking in subdued tones as if in a church. From time to time someone would go to the safety room door and peer anxiously out wishing for a hasty return of the Second Officer, every minute felt like an hour. Their demeanour was not helped by hearing further explosions, and seeing more crew hurrying passed dressed in survival gear. At last the Second Officer appeared very much out of breath and sweating profusely.

"You're right Chief, it sure is no bloody picnic up there on deck, in fact, it's one big hell of a mess" he gasped out.

"I know, I know, I saw it all before on my way to the gas bottle room. Never mind all that, what has the bridge got to say?" the Chief said somewhat irritably.

"Nothing specific, the only important thing the Captain did say was for me to advise you Chief to collect as much warm clothing as possible for your party and put it on."

"Thats sounds ominous" said Charles.

The Chief looked at Charles and nodded slightly "Right then, Charles you take the fourth engineer with you and collect all the warm gear you can find in our accommodation and bring it back to this mustering point as quickly as you can. The rest of the party get to your cabins and grab all your warm gear and report back to me."

Charles did not need any second bidding "Lets go Keith no time to lose, we will start at the Chief's cabin and work our way down to ours, keep me in sight all the time" Charles tried to sound calm and collected but his insides were churning away full ahead. "This is not what I signed on for" he complained to himself. They hurriedly went up into the accommodation on the fifth deck and straight into the Chief's cabin, which he had been sharing with the second engineer, opened up the wardrobes and grabbed all the anoraks and warm jumpers they could find and stuffed them into the plastic bags they had brought with them. They also picked up two plastic bags containing arctic clothing which had been issued to them by the Navy.

"OK Keith, next stop the "thirds" cabin and then the electricians" Charles ordered.

The atmosphere was still heavily smoke laden but the visibility was reasonably good but the heat was still intense. Having collected all that was needed from those two cabins Charles turned to Keith.

"Now you go to your cabin and grab all you want and I will go into mine, it will be a lot quicker that way and it's only next door, if you get stuck just give me a shout"

They then descended to the fourth deck where their cabins were, Charles walked through the doorway of his cabin, the door was still hanging drunkenly on its broken hinges and it suddenly reminded him of his aching shoulder caused by crashing through it to escape from his cabin. With all that had been happening these past hours he had completely forgotten the pain in his shoulder. He took all the clothing he knew he would require for his survival when suddenly he had the most urgent desire to use the bathroom "This is absolute bliss I have been bursting to go ever since the emergency alarm went off" he said to himself as he emptied his bladder. Whilst he was experiencing this magic moment the Fourth Engineer was bellowing from the doorway.

"Hurry up Charles, for Christ's sake hurry up."

With a sigh of sheer relief and stopping only to flush the toilet, he rejoined him and they began to make their way back down to the mustering point. On their way they were stopped by a person already completely dressed for survival and looking at them rather suspiciously. Because the hood of his survival suit was on it was difficult for Charles to ascertain who he was.

"What do you have in those bags?" he enquired in a very imperious voice Charles immediately recognised him from his voice as one of the "Conveyor" officers. The Fourth Engineer gave him a malevolent glare and completely ignored him.

"They are full of warm clothing for all the engineers at their mustering point in case we are ordered to abandon ship; you are pretty well kitted up I see." Charles got the impression that this haughty figure did not believe him and he thought we were looting the cabins. Charles was incensed at his stance and attitude "What the hell do you think we are doing" The officer made no reply but continued to stand in front of them. Charles's patience had run out with this individual "How can anyone think we are looting our fellow officers cabins in the situation we are in" thought Charles.

"We have no time to lose, I can't stand here all day arguing with you what we have or don't have in these bags move out of the way" Charles said in no uncertain terms and they brusquely pushed passed him. He offered no resistance or attempted to stop them.

"If I ever have the misfortune to come across that bastard again I will thump him" Charles said heatedly to Keith.

They arrived back at the safety room and distributed the various belongings to the people concerned, the crew members who had been detailed to collect their warm clothing had all returned safely.

"Well done Charles, you did a great job, and you too fourth" said the Chief.

"No problem Chief it had to be done by someone" they both replied matter-of-factly.

The Chief looked at the both of them with the greatest of admiration.

"I could not have asked for a better set of engineers than I have here" he said to himself.

12

ABANDON SHIP

Down in the cargo decks the fire was now raging out of control, the damage control parties had fought tenaciously and bravely, in the most horrendous and dangerous conditions, in their attempt to contain the fires but it was a fight against hopeless odds. Explosions were occurring frequently in the cargo decks as one thing or another exploded in the heat, and the fire was advancing rapidly towards the main bomb and fuel storage decks in the forward bays. Despite their valiant efforts it became clear to them that they had lost the battle against the fires. Accordingly they contacted the bridge and informed them of the terrifying situation in the cargo decks and that they could do no more. Captain North reacted immediately, ordering the Chief Officer to inform the ship's company over the Public Address system to abandon ship.

Charles and the rest of the party at the mustering point had put on their warm clothing and had commenced struggling into their survival suits and lifejackets. It was not an easy task and everyone was concerned that this unfamiliar apparel was being put on correctly. They all heard the abandon ship order. Charles turned to the Second Engineer who was next to him and still struggling to get his gear on.

"Not before bloody time if you ask me Graham, the deck is getting hotter by the minute beneath us."

"It sure is, I can feel the heat through my rubber suit, boots, and socks"
The reason for the excessive heat was because the uncontrollable flames had
caught hold of the cargo under the wooden deck sections they were standing
on.

"What do you think the weather's like outside Graham?" asked Charles.

"I have not got a clue, you'd better go and have a look yourself and let us
know."

Charles moved towards the open door and glanced outside to the deck. It was
pitch black outside and all he could see was spray coming on deck from the
waves, which did not help his confidence one bit, and the daunting prospect
of going into it made him shiver uncontrollably.

"What's the weather like outside then?" enquired the Chief.

"It's bloody awful, it's pitch black, we are shipping spray from the waves and
it's damned cold. I don't know how we are ever going to get away in those
conditions". Charles was beginning to convince himself that he was not
going to survive.

"We can't be shipping spray she's hardly rolling, let me have a look."

The Chief went to the doorway and peered out. He came back with a smile
on his face. "You are quite right Charles it is dark outside and bloody cold
but we are not shipping spray from the waves, what you were actually
looking at was a naval frigate pulling away from the side of us with all her
fire hoses going full ahead aimed at us."

"Thank God for that" a relieved Charles said.

There were quite a number of people milling about in the doorway leading
out to the main deck, then Charles and the engine room party made an
orderly way on to the deck. Charles spotted one of the cooks looking
somewhat apprehensive. "Hi cookie how is it going? You look a bit
worried."

"I am worried I don't know if I have got this damn survival suit on properly."

"As far as I can see it looks OK to me, it's no good asking you if my gear is on properly if you don't know if yours is" Charles said with a smile. There were lots of people on the main deck but what amazed Charles most of all was the incredible calm of everyone. The majority of them were quite young, they had never heard a shot fired in anger in their lives nor had they ever been on a ship that was sinking and sinking into freezing seas.

Suddenly a Naval Petty Officer standing next to Charles started shouting "Don't panic, Don't panic" on the top of his voice. It reminded Charles of Corporal Jones in the television comedy "Dads Army". Whether he was actually starting to panic himself or just making a joke of it all Charles did not know and being in his own circumstances he could not care less. His greatest concern was the effect this outburst was having on those standing around him. Charles noticed it was causing unnecessary alarm and he could see anxious expressions appearing on a number of faces of the people around him. Charles spun round and elbowed the Petty Officer.

" Will you effing well shut up, you bloody idiot" he said furiously " Can't you see you are scaring the shit out of some of the men here and only making the whole situation a bloody sight worse."

The Petty Officer was taken aback at the verbal onslaught on him and looked quite abashed but to Charles's delight he never said another word.

Charles sized up the situation and quickly spoke to the Chief Engineer.

"We will have to get this lot into some sort of order or none of us will be getting off."

"I can see that. What's the best thing we can do?"

"There are three Jacob ladders lowered down over the starboard side of the ship, to start with we will get this mob into three queues as fast and as orderly as we can, possibly do it at the head of each ladder."

Charles and the Chief immediately began herding all the people into three queues, it was no easy task, as everyone was trying to be first in the queue and therefore first off the ship. There was a lot of shoving and pushing and cursing at the head of each queue. "Hey you guys take it easy, the way you are all pushing and shoving the longer it's going to take for all of us to get off. Just calm down and take it easy". Charles's shouted orders seemed to have the desired effect on the jostling crowd, they began to quieten down and get in line without too much pushing and shoving.

There was no launching of lifeboats, it was considered safer and faster to use rafts, which were attached by a rope to the ship and inflated automatically when they hit the water. There were some of these inflatable rafts visible to Charles but they were ahead of the Jacob ladders which the crew were waiting to descend. The ship was wallowing quite a bit in the swell that had now got up and there was a very stiff and bitterly cold wind blowing making their position even more untenable. Charles looked over the side once again, a chap who had been doing the perfect breast stroke was now lying face down in the freezing water, he was not moving at all.

"Poor beggar he must have frozen to death" Charles said to himself, but he had no time to linger on this morbid thought. The life rafts had gradually drifted towards the Jacob ladders and it was time for Charles and the Chief to get the men over the side and into the life rafts.

"OK you guys let's get moving" ordered the Chief.

One by one they climbed on to the ships rail and went over the side on to the Jacob ladders and started to descend into the life rafts. Suddenly Charles was startled by someone bellowing from the bridge "Don't wait for the ladders, jump, go on, jump for it." Charles was convinced if they did that there was going to be a terrific loss of life, it was about forty five feet from the deck down to the freezing sea.

"Hold it you guys, ignore what you heard from the bridge, just keep going over the side on to the ladders" Charles firmly ordered.

The crew took heed of Charles's advice and continued to wait their turn to get on to the ladders with praiseworthy calm and patience. They were standing in about six inches of water "It's a good thing this water is swilling about Chief, otherwise the heat from the deck would be burning our feet off" remarked Charles.

"Aye you're right, this water must be coming from the fire pumps, which by some miracle must be still running."

Some Royal Naval people had joined the evacuation party to help the Chief and Charles get the men up on to the rail and over the side. At last it was Charles time to be helped up on to the rail and start climbing down the ladder. Charles was very appreciative of this assistance." Thanks for the leg up, it's bloody difficult getting over the side with all this extra gear on."

"No problem sir, glad to be of assistance old boy" said the fruity voice of the smiling officer, just as if he had helped an old lady across a busy road. Charles never felt comfortable on ladders, even when painting at home, if he ever had to use a ladder he did it very reluctantly and with much trepidation. His descent down the Jacob's ladder became one of the most unpleasant experiences he ever had to endure. He had managed to get down about four

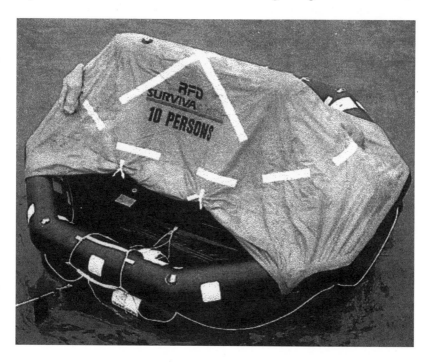

The above self inflating raft, supplied by RFD Belfast,
was carried on the 'Atlantic Conveyor'. The front opening is how Charles Drought
entered the raft after jumping from the blazing vessel. The line attaching the raft to
the vessel can be seen in the bottom left hand corner.

rungs when he became very aware that the ship was rolling about more than he had anticipated.

The ladder began to swing like a pendulum and it crashed him against the ships side a number of times, Charles was hanging on for dear life gripping the rope part of the ladder, the wooden rungs crashed into the ships side first and this prevented him from getting his hands smashed. To add to his woes the transparent face shield which was part of the life jacket had broken loose from its Velcro fastenings and was flapping about in the wind smacking him in the face. He could not do anything about it as both his hands were in use. Because his face shield had come adrift there was a foul smelling and tasting liquid being blown in a spray into his face from the direction of the stern, he immediately recognised it as aviation spirit which was being jettisoned from tanks on the after deck to reduce the risk of the fire hazard that would blow the ship up if it reached the tanks.

"Dear God is there anything else that can happen to me" he swore. Little did he realise what was before him!

Charles continued his descent until he was approximately ten feet above the water, he could see the life raft bobbing about directly beneath him, but he sensed that there was something amiss with the ladder his left foot had met with no resistance "There must be a rung missing" he thought. Other people were continuing their descent down the ladder, he grabbed hold of the ankle of the man immediately above.

"Hold on a minute will you" he shouted " I think there is something wrong with the ladder a rung or rungs are missing".

The descent down the ladder came to an abrupt halt and Charles looked down to see what was wrong, he could just make out that the left hand rope had parted completely and the lower part of the ladder was a mass of splintered wood and had twisted around and Charles was now only being supported by the right hand rope.

"OK lads I am going to continue down the ladder, but watch your step the bottom half of the ladder is knackered hardly any undamaged rungs" he called to the waiting men on the ladder. What had actually happened 'HMS Alacrity' had come alongside the 'Conveyor' to train all her fire hoses on the burning vessel and if possible to transfer men directly from ship to ship. Unfortunately with the weather conditions deteriorating this manoeuvre had to be abandoned and she had to back off. It was during this attempt of ship to ship rescue she had smashed into the Jacob's ladders that had been lowered over the side destroying the whole of the lower parts.

"Well here goes" Charles murmured and took one step to the right and continued down the ladder when he came to the mangled part of the ladder the rope that was supporting him began to fray and suddenly it parted completely. There was nothing else Charles could do to prevent his falling from the ladder instinctively he kicked out at the side of the ship hurtling down and landing with a jarring thump on his back in a ignominious heap inside the doorway of a life raft, the wind completely knocked out of him.

13

THE LIFE RAFT TRAUMA

Charles was still winded and slightly disorientated from the trauma of all that had happened to him over the last few hours, he scrambled on to his hands and knees and with some difficulty, because the base of the raft was very soft like a bed mattress and the raft was bobbing about in the swell, he managed to stand upright. He checked himself all over and found no broken bones but his shoulder from breaking down his cabin door was throbbing painfully.

He staggered to the doorway of the raft and looked out, the sight that met him was of utter confusion and one which he would never forget. He could see thick black smoke pouring out of every opening on the 'Conveyor' as she lay dead in the water wallowing in the seas. The heat from the raging fires inside her was making her sides red hot and Charles could see that the Jacob's ladders were beginning to catch fire. People were still coming down the ladders but those on the lower parts of the ladders were just standing still transfixed with fear looking at their fellow crew members swimming and splashing about in the freezing sea and through the considerable swell.

"Jump, for Christ's sake jump, you've got to jump now or you will never make it" Charles screamed at them.

The petrified men on the ladders heard Charles's shout and one by one they leapt off the smouldering ladders into the freezing sea. He saw the first man leap off the ladder backwards into the sea and he disappeared.

"Oh no" he said to himself "they are all going to drown, please God don't let them drown".

To Charles's great relief, as if his fervent prayer had been answered, the man reappeared and doing a sort of ' doggie paddle' struck out to his raft. As he came closer Charles recognised him as the second steward , Eddy Jarvis, he kept stopping his paddling to push his glasses back on.

"Never mind your bloody glasses keep swimming towards me" shouted Charles. He kept shouting encouragement to him all the time to keep swimming towards him. He had almost reached the raft when the raft was lifted high up on top of the swell and he disappeared, the raft came crashing into the trough between the swells knocking Charles off his feet on to the bottom of the raft again, struggling upright again he saw that Eddy had reappeared again right in front of him. He leant out over the flotation collar of the raft and just managed to get a hold of his hand.

"Hang on to me Eddy and I will pull you in" shouted Charles, but just then the raft reared up on to the top of a bigger swell and he lost his grip on the struggling Eddy. The raft crashed down again but this time right on top of Eddy, Charles feared the worst that this time he would not resurface but unbelievably Eddy surfaced again, minus his spectacles, and he caught hold of one of the grab lines which hung all the way round the raft.

"Drag yourself around to the doorway Eddy and I will be able to lean right out and grab you."

His progress was painfully slow and Charles was beginning to fear another big swell would arrive and lift the raft up and he would lose his already tenuous grip on the grab line, he knew time was running out for Eddy; he could see he was getting weaker by the minute with all his exertions and the deadly cold. At last Eddy arrived at the doorway of the raft completely exhausted. Life rafts are very difficult to get into from the water, more so when dressed in all the survival gear. There is a rope ladder at each entrance but they were now lying flat on the underside of the raft. Charles leant out over the collar of the raft grabbed hold of him and with one mighty heave, which sent the pain racing through his damaged shoulder, he hauled him aboard and they both fell into the bottom of the raft absolutely breathless. Eddy could hardly speak but the look on his face as he turned to Charles spoke volumes of his eternal gratitude towards Charles for certainly saving his life.

They lay there for a short while getting their breath back, Charles knew the raft was still secured to the 'Conveyor' by the inflation line and this needed to be cut in order to free themselves from the ship that any moment might blow up.

"Eddy, I am racking my brain here trying to remember from all those bloody safety films we were eternally shown were the hell is the special knife kept, the one we need to cut us free from the 'Conveyor' before she blows up and we go up with her, can you remember where they said it was stowed."

"Not really, but I do recall something about it being in some sort of a pocket near one of the access doors."

"Right then, I'll look into the pocket near me and you check out the pocket near you, if it's not there I'll start searching along this side and you get searching along your side" a worried Charles ordered.

It was not going to be an easy task in the dark as trying to walk around the raft was nigh on impossible, the footing was like a giant sponge and the raft was heaving up and down in the swell making their task even harder.

"We will have to crawl around on our hands and knees Eddy, that's going to be the easiest and fastest way."

"OK let's get to it."

They were still scrambling around looking for the knife when some-one climbed into the raft all professionally kitted up.

"Who the hell are you?" a startled Charles exclaimed.

"I'm the duty diver from the 'Alacrity', he calmly replied "are you chaps all right in here?"

Charles was really taken aback at this sudden and unexpected appearance of the diver." Yes we are OK, but we can't find the knife to cut us free from the ship."

"Don't worry about that, I'll do that for you, and when you are free try and keep together with all the other rafts if you can". To Charles's astonishment he shouted "Good Luck" and dived through the doorway into the sea again.

Charles was watching him go when he heard a thick Scottish voice coming from behind him "Charlie is that you" it said.

Charles turned around and peering through the gloom at this dishevelled figure, he at once recognised the Chief Engineer.

"Chief" exclaimed an amazed Charles "how the hell did you manage to climb aboard without any help?"

"Aye it's me alright and a bloody cold and wet me too, it was one hell of a struggle to get aboard I can tell you."

"If I had heard or seen you trying to get in, struggling on your own I would have given you a heave up over the collar" Charles was really pleased to see that Jim had made it, be it only this far.

"No problem Charlie you seem to have your own problems, what's the situation here?"

"I can't find the knife to cut us free from the ship, Eddy the Second Steward is helping me look for it but a Royal Navy diver off the 'Alacrity' came aboard to check us out, I told him we couldn't find the knife and he said not to bother he would cut us free and I was watching him dive back out when you were crawling aboard, that's why I didn't see you" explained Charles. "Did he say anything else what we have to do?"

" He said we must make contact with the other rafts and all keep together" "That seems sensible enough" replied the Chief.

"I am going to stay in this doorway and help anyone else to get aboard you stand by your doorway and do the same, Eddy isn't looking too good he was a long time in the water".

Eddy was huddled in a corner of the raft shivering uncontrollably and looking very pale. Charles thought 'if we don't get him aboard another ship soon he is not going to make it'. He looked out of his doorway again to see a helicopter hovering above them directing a searchlight on to the sea and he could see divers going between the rafts checking if any help was needed. Other helicopters hovered above winching men out of the sea and out of the rafts. A helicopter landed on the forward flight deck of the blazing 'Conveyor' and took off the forward fire party, an act of incredible bravery, with the possibility that the ship could blow up at any moment and without a thought for their own safety, they snatched the forward fire party to safety from the blazing 'Conveyor'.

The weather conditions continued to deteriorate and Charles noticed huge flames were now spouting out from the 'Conveyor'. He had not seen any fire while he was aboard the ship only dense black smoke and he never thought the 'Conveyor' would sink but seeing the flames he realised there was no saving her and she would eventually go down.

The raft was drifting to the stern of the ship still attached by the inflation line and Charles could see a bright light all around the massive stern ramp doors he knew it was the fire that was raging through "C" deck that was showing through the edges of the doors. This increased his fears that if they were not cut adrift soon they would all be lost.

"Where in the hell is that bloody naval diver?" he said to himself.

To his right about 50 yards away he saw a cluster of rafts wallowing about in the swell and drifting towards him; he could see people in the water hanging on to the grab lines of the rafts, with the rafts surging up and down in the swell, some of them could hold on no longer in the freezing sea, they lost their grip and floated away out of sight. Slowly, but agonisingly slowly, the cluster of rafts came nearer and nearer to Charles when suddenly the same Royal Navy Diver who had boarded his raft earlier appeared alongside his raft.

"I have cut you free now, keep together and we will get you aboard the 'Alacrity' safely" he shouted and threw the line to Charles. He waved, gave the thumbs up sign and swam away before Charles had a chance to thank him.

Charles caught hold of the rope that the Diver had thrown to him and called out "Chief will you and anybody else come over here and lend a hand to haul on this rope so we can get alongside the other rafts."

"On my way Charles" replied the Chief.

To Charles's surprise Eddy crawled from the corner of the raft and took hold of the rope, "Are you OK Eddy" asked a concerned Charles, he did not say anything but just nodded his head. The three of them began to haul on the rope, hand over hand, for what seemed an eternity to Charles, until at last they came alongside the other surviving rafts. He slumped down on to the base of the raft completely exhausted from his exertions, the freezing conditions were beginning to get to him, he found himself shivering and getting drowsy and he knew that this was a dangerous sign that hypothermia was setting in from the deadly exposure to the cold.

"Are you OK Charles?" he heard a voice say. He looked up into the face of the Chief who was kneeling beside him looking anxiously into his eyes.

" Yes Chief, just a bit knackered but I will be all right, I've got to keep moving" He shook his head violently to clear any of the symptoms of drowsiness and struggled to his feet with a little assistance from the Chief.

"I will get back to my doorway then, OK Charles?"

"Sure thing Chief I am feeling OK, now I have got my breath back. Let's try and haul as many guys as we can out of the water."

Charles looked outside again to see if he could help any men in the water, he could see the blazing stern of the 'Conveyor' and the swell was tending to make the ship rise and fall causing the rafts to be pushed towards the ship and away again. He turned away from the doorway and spoke to Eddy "You OK now? You looked bloody awful a minute ago I thought you were going to snuff it".

"I thought I was going to ring 'finished with engines' too, I felt terrible but I have got over that now and I am ready for anything".

"You know what I have just realised Eddy?"

"No, what."

"I have left my wedding ring in the cabin" bemoaned Charles.

"So what for Christ's sake, you can always buy another one, don't worry about it, you are reasonably safe here and that's all that matters."

"But it won't be the same or have the same feeling". bemoaned Charles "I wonder if I could get back on board and get it?"

"Don't be a bloody fool 3rd, its not only impossible but suicidal as well."

"I suppose you are right" Charles said and heaved a deep troubled sigh.

"I don't suppose I am right I bloody well know I am right" admonished Eddy.

"Another thing Eddy, I left sixty five quid in my desk as well."

"Now that is a tragedy, think of all the ale you could have bought me with that little lot " said Eddy, trying to make light of Charles's dilemmas and lift his moral." "But no, seriously 3rd, you are here, forget all about what you have left behind on the ship and let's get to that ship out there."

"You are right Eddy let's get to it."

The rafts which they had eventually pulled themselves alongside, were low in the water and crowded with survivors in various states of exhaustion and exposure. There were men lying on top of one another. Charles caught hold of the grab-lines of the nearest raft to him and hung on tightly, but the cold soon made his hands cramped, so he pushed his arms through the ropes and held on that fashion, he could not afford to let go in case they drifted away from the other rafts and were lost into the darkness beyond the searchlights of the helicopters. Opposite Charles, in the door way of the raft he was holding on to, a young Royal Navy Petty Officer appeared and took hold of Charles's raft in a similar fashion. His face was only a few feet away from his.

"Thanks that's a great help" shouted Charles, his only reply was a little nod of his head and a slight smile.

"That has to be some guy" thought Charles.

There was some sort of activity going on in the adjacent raft.The occupants of the next raft, including Phil Bailey, had just hauled in one of the Chinese laundrymen and he was in a really bad way. They were trying to bring him round by the artificial respiration method, but with the floor of the raft heaving about all over the place they unfortunately failed to revive him.

Shrugging these morbid thoughts out of his mind he returned to his own predicament and shouted to the Petty Officer clinging to his raft.

"Hey! How about getting some of your blokes into our raft, that should relieve the overcrowding, you are pretty low in the water?"

"Good idea I'll give them a shout". He could do no more, hanging on to the raft as he was. Charles heard him shouting if any of his survivors would like to transfer over to his raft to relieve the crowding and make their raft safer. No one came forward.

A dramatic picture of a Sea King helicopter rescuing
survivors from the blazing 'Atlantic Conveyor'

"Nobody wants to come over, they think they have their hold on life in their own raft, albeit a tenuous one, and looking at the sea conditions, they are not going to let go of it" the Petty Officer replied almost apologetically.

"I don't suppose I can blame them."

For the next two hours they hardly spoke at all, they remained with their arms linked through the grab-lines, they were continuously being tossed up and down in the swell, a number of times Charles thought his arms were going to be wrenched from their sockets, but he hung on grimly knowing that his grip on the grab-lines meant the difference between life and death for all those in his raft. The numbing cold was acting like an anaesthetic to the pain in his injured shoulder and in his present predicament had little time to dwell on his injury although he did feel the occasional twinge but this did not weaken him from his determination to hold on to the other raft.

The Chief with the help of others were pulling survivors out of the water and dragging them into the raft. In a very short while the raft became dangerously overcrowded and they had to stop rescuing any more men in the water. He noticed one man struggling in the swell towards the raft, he made a grab for the raft but missed and went under the sea, he came up gasping for breath and made another, now very weak, effort to clutch at the raft. Jim realised he was not going to make it on his own, he leant over the collar of the raft as far as he safely could and stretched out his arms.

"Here grab hold of me" he shouted to the weakening man in the water and with a last despairing effort he managed to clutch Jim's arms and hold on for dear life as he pulled him alongside the raft. Because there was no more room inside the raft, for the next hour, Jim supported the totally exhausted man's head and upper part of his body across the collar of the raft, the lower part of his body still being in the water.

Eventually, to Charles's utter delight and relief their group of rafts was illuminated by a searchlight from a hovering helicopter and he could just make out a large dark shape not too far away looming up to his left.

"I hope to hell that's the rescue ship coming for us" he said to himself. As they slowly wallowed their way towards the dark ship, Charles recognised it was a warship, and it turned out to be 'HMS Alacrity', the same one that had attempted to come alongside the 'Conveyor' to rescue the crew, the Captain bravely standing by the stricken ship all the time.

Charles still hanging on grimly, heard a series of small explosions and immediately knew that on the warship they were ingeniously firing Coston gun lines over to the rafts to help them haul themselves alongside and clamber aboard. Charles had seen the naval ships practising this manoeuvre for getting lines ashore when docking in Plymouth and at sea between ships when they were refuelling on their way down to the Falklands. Unfortunately, in all the confusion, one of the crew in the raft was cutting any lines that came aboard, Charles saw what was happening out of the corner of his eye.

"What the hell do you think you are doing?" he screamed at him.

"I'm cutting the lines that are connecting us to the 'Conveyor' sir."

"Stop that you stupid idiot, they are not the lines from the 'Conveyor' they are the lines shot over from that warship out there to help us haul over to their side" Charles riled at him.

"Oh hell, I'm sorry sir I thought I was helping" said a much admonished and contrite crew man.

"Dear God what next is going to happen" thought Charles.

As the warship drew closer Charles could see a scrambling net hanging over the ships side. "That's going to take some effort climbing up that bloody thing" thought Charles.

At the other doorway the Chief spoke to the survivor he was holding on to.

"Can you manage to hold on by yourself now, just for a minute or two, I have to help to get us alongside that ship and then you will be OK?"

He looked up into Jim's face, he couldn't speak, he weakly nodded his head and took a firmer grip of the rafts collar.

"Charles, when we get close enough grab the net and I will do the same on my side" shouted the Chief.

"No can do Chief, like I told you before my hands are full hanging on to this other raft."

"Well get some other bugger to do it" rasped the Chief.

"Will do. Eddy you heard what the Chief said you stand by to make a grab for the net."

"OK 3rd" the ever willing Eddy replied.

The warship was constantly manoeuvring itself to give the life rafts as much lee as possible. One of the rafts in the group to the left had managed to get hold of a life line from the 'Alacrity' and some others to the right had successfully caught hold of some life lines. Slowly and agonisingly the gap between the rafts and the warship closed.

"OK Eddy grab hold of the scramble net I've got a hold on my side" shouted the Chief.

Eddy leant out of the raft and caught hold of the net with as firm a grip as his frozen hands would allow. "Got it Chief" he shouted back.

"Good lad, hang on in there, we've nearly made it."

Charles's arms were still interlocked with the grab lines of the next raft, every muscle and every sinew in his arms ached intolerably with the cold and hanging on so long but he was very reluctant to let go for fear of losing contact with the main body of the rafts when so near to being rescued as he could see a whole mass of rafts alongside the warship.

Charles looked at the young Petty Officer holding on to his raft just as tenaciously "Nearly there pal, won't be long now before we are safely aboard" encouraged Charles.

"Thank God for that my arms are nearly dropping off" was his stoic reply. Suddenly, to both their complete amazement, someone from inside his raft roughly shoved Charles to one side and climbed over the top him.

"Hey, where the hell do you think you are going matey?" an enraged Charles shouted at him, "Can't you wait your bloody turn?"

Completely ignoring this exhortation, the man jumped on both of Charles's arms. He let out a howl of pain, but the man was completely oblivious to the pain he had inflicted on Charles. From Charles's arms he launched himself at the scrambling net, caught hold of it and quickly started to climb upwards. Charles recognised who he was, it was one of the high ranking Naval officers they had on board the 'Conveyor'.

He had got about half way up, when he lost his grip and fell back, screaming with fear, on to the roof of the raft.

"Serves you bloody well right, you selfish bastard", thought an enraged Charles, the pain still throbbing in his arms. He was particularly annoyed that the man had seen fit to use him as a sort of a springboard to get to the net first and his outright lack of concern for no-one other than himself. From the roof of the raft the panicking Naval officer caught hold of the scrambling net again and climbed successfully up on to the deck of the 'Alacrity', his cowardly actions had made him the first to arrive on the rescue ship.

"Did you see that?" asked Charles in total disbelief of what he had seen, to the Petty Officer in the other raft.

"I did, and I know who the cowardly bastard was" was his grim reply. "Hardly the conduct of a Senior Naval Officer or in the best traditions of the Royal Navy."

"True, but there is always one in any service that lets you down when you least expect it."

Before they could say any more they heard a loud explosion coming from the 'Conveyor'.

"Jesus, I hope she's not going to go up now" Charles prayed.

The 'Alacrity', during her manoeuvring to give the rafts the best lee and to close the gap between the 'Conveyor' and themselves and the survivors on the raft, was now lying very close to the 'Conveyor'. Fearing that the

'Conveyor' was about to explode with all its cargo of bombs and fuel and their close proximity to this floating bomb, the safety of his ship and all her crew was foremost in Commander Chris Craig's reactions. Taking the microphone for the Public Address system he announced.

"We are about to go full astern, all rafts let go of the scramble net and release the life lines" he repeated this message several times.

"For Christ's sake Chief, what's he up to now we have only just got alongside?" exploded Charles.

"Haven't got a clue Charles, but just do as he says, and quickly or we will be pulled under."

"How many times have I got to tell you Chief, I can't do a damn thing to help you, I am still hanging on to this other raft."

"Well let go of it then" he shouted back.

Charles spoke to the Petty Officer holding on to his raft. "The Chief wants us to let go of each other before we get pulled under with that ship going full astern is that OK with you?"

"I think that's a good idea, we're pretty safe now with all these other rafts around us and besides, I don't think I can hold on much longer the whole of my arms have gone numb with the strain of holding on and the cold."

"It's the same with me, OK then, see you around pal."

They both relinquished their hold on each others raft and without a moments respite, even though he could feel no sensation at all in his arms, Charles helped to push the raft away from the ship that was now going full astern, he was quickly followed by all the other rafts that had been clinging to the net. At that moment Charles heard a long drawn out scream that sent a shiver down his spine, a scream that would forever remain in his memory. He looked towards the scrambling net and saw one of the life lines still attached to a raft had snapped as the ship went full astern and had wrapped itself around a survivor who was still clinging on half way up the net, the line plucked him off the net, and smashed him against the ship's side, the scream stopped abruptly and he fell into the sea. Charles waited for him to resurface but he did not reappear and Charles never saw him again.

"Poor devil to be so very, very near to being rescued and for that to happen" a sad Charles said to himself.

He had no time to reflect on this tragic incident. The helicopter had continued to hover above them and keep its search light illuminating them, and the 'Alacrity' had completed its manoeuvring and was returning to the survivors rafts. He knew the most important task was to get alongside the rescue ship and get aboard as quickly as possible.

'H. M. S. Alacrity'
The Rescue Ship

14

ON BOARD THE HMS ALACRITY

The 'Alacrity' again fired more Coston lines over the rafts as she approached them and Charles and the Chief managed to take a hold of two of them.

"Hang on tight Charles and heave away for all your worth, we are not going to let go this time for whatever reason or whoever orders us to do it" bellowed the Chief.

"You can say that again Chief."

Charles heaved away on his line, the sensations were coming back to his arms and so was the pain in his shoulder. Once more the gap between the raft and the ship slowly narrowed, other rafts were already alongside and Charles noticed that the crew on the ship were operating a winch of some sort. He saw the body of the man that he thought he recognised as the one he had seen floating face down in the sea when he had first left the 'Conveyor' from the clothes it was wearing, being hoisted aboard and then it came down again to lift someone else from the sea.

"I wonder if that's the poor devil that got torn off the net?" thought Charles.

At last they managed to get alongside the ship and the scramble net. Charles leaned out and grabbed the net and saw that the Chief had done the same from his doorway. Hanging on tightly, he shouted to Eddy "OK Eddy let go, you get on to the net and climb aboard."

Eddy did not need a second bidding with an agility that even surprised Charles, after all he had been through, he stood between Charles's arms on the flotation collar and threw himself at the net and swiftly climbed upwards to the safety of the ship's deck.

The Chief was still hanging on to the net at his doorway, when a Royal Navy man they had pulled out of the sea earlier, scrambled across the raft and spoke to Charles.

"I think it would be best if you let go here now and we will all go out from the other doorway."

Charles had some misgivings about this manoeuvre "Do you really think that's a good idea?"

"Yes I do, it will be the quickest and easiest way to get off this raft, trust me I have seen this done in training" he answered assuredly.

"OK if you say so, but I hope you know what you are doing."

"I do, just trust me."

Charles very reluctantly let go of the net and the raft immediately spun alarmingly around and Charles found himself facing the open sea again.

"Trust you, trust you, you bloody well said" yelled a very frightened Charles at the Navy man.

Before the Navy man could make a reply the raft was hit by a huge wave which rose up beneath them sending them hurtling upwards, as the raft fell back into the trough another tremendous wave came crashing through the doorway with the force of a sledge hammer, it threw Charles face down in the bottom of the raft. They had been almost completely overwhelmed by that wave.

Charles, spluttering and struggling, got on to his knees, cursing the Navy man's idea of letting one end go. "Why the hell did I listen to him" he said to himself. He tried to stand up but with about four inches of seawater sloshing about the sponge-like surface of the raft he found this an impossibility. He crawled across to the doorway where the Chief and the Navy man had a secure hold on the scramble netting.

"I wish to Christ I'd never listened to you and your bloody daft ideas" a soaking wet Charles glowered at the Navy man.

"I am sorry about the soaking you got, but you wait and see it will be as I said" he replied with great conviction. Charles was still very dubious about the whole thing.

"Never mind the chit-chat, let's get this raft emptied and the men on to the net before another wave comes along and sinks us this time" shouted the Chief.

"OK, OK, don't get your knickers in a twist" Charles jokingly rebuked the Chief.

"I'll twist your knickers if you don't get a bloody move on" the Chief replied smiling. One by one, with a little help from Charles, the Chief and the Navy man, the remaining survivors smoothly exited the raft on to the scramble net and up to the safety of the ship.

"Right then, its you now, off you go" Charles said to the Naval Officer he held his arm to steady him on the raft collar.

"Before you go, I just want to say you were right after all, this is the best way for everyone to leave the raft by using the one doorway, I am sorry I doubted you".

"You don't have to be sorry old chap, its all in my training but thank you all the same". He shook Charles warmly by the hand, smiled and leapt on the scramble net. The helicopter that had been hovering above them with its searchlight had left as soon as he saw all the rafts were safely alongside the rescue ship. Charles watched anxiously as he made his way up the darkened side of the ship and then he disappeared into the darkness above. Charles never met him again.

Charles turned around to the Chief, "You know what Chief, I don't even know that guy's name."

"So what, neither do I, does it matter?"

Charles thought for a moment, shrugged his shoulders and said "Nope I suppose not but I still think it would have been nice to know his name. Anyway, it's your turn to go Chief, you are soaking wet, you had a hell of a struggle getting into the raft and you are blue with the freezing cold, get going."

"No way Charlie, I'll be all right, you go first."

"But I am concerned about the state you are in."

"You heard me Charlie, get going" the Chief abruptly replied.

Charles could see how determined he was for him to leave first and it was no use trying to persuade him otherwise "It's that Scottish stubborn streak in him that they are all born with that makes him like this" Charles said to himself.

"Charlie, for God's sake get going" he urged "we are wasting valuable time here arguing with each other and trying to be ever so bloody gentlemanly."

"Right I am off."

Charles climbed up on to the collar of the raft and leapt upwards and caught hold of the mesh rungs and started to laboriously climb up the swaying side of the ship. He was finding it difficult to obtain a good grip on the net because he was still wearing his anti-flash gauntlets that had filled with water when the wave crashed into the raft knocking him to the floor, he had emptied them but the dampness inside them was making his fingers stiff and begin to cramp. The pain in his arms from holding onto the raft when they crossed over to the rescue ship was becoming almost unbearable and his injured shoulder throbbed agonisingly with the strain of the effort of pulling himself up the netting.

Charles reached a point where he could no longer move, the pain was so excruciating in his arms made any movement at all beyond him. Utterly exhausted and racked with pain he linked his arms through the mesh and hung there gasping in pain. The rolling ship and biting cold only made Charles's condition worse and at this moment he felt that he was not going to survive and that this was the end. A sailor appeared on the deck of the rescue ship and looked over the side and saw Charles clinging to the scramble net,

"Are you all right mate" he shouted to Charles.

He looked up to see who was shouting to him and from where and was surprised to find he was only a few feet from the top of the net.

"Are you all right mate" the voice repeated.

"No, I can't move, I'm buggered" an anguished Charles replied.

"You will be all right, just take it easy for a while and rest there."

The sailor stood watching Charles very closely for a few minutes.

"Come on now mister, keep moving you are nearly there, you'll be all right, you'll make it" he called out encouragingly.

Charles looked up at him forlornly, when suddenly an extraordinary thing occurred, the sailor's face changed to that of Betty's with the light shining behind her as it did on their last night together and he heard her say "You'll be all right darling, you will make it."

Charles could hardly believe it, but he knew he could not give up now, he must make it for Betty's sake. He suddenly found a new energy, he pulled his aching arms out of the netting and with all the waning strength left in him, he forced himself to clamber up the remaining couple feet on to the deck of the ship and fell into the arms of the sailor who had been standing above him shouting encouragement.

"There you are matey, I told you you could make it" he smiled at Charles.

"Only bloody just" he gasped out, still amazed and not a little bemused at seeing Betty and hearing her voice. Charles stared at the young sailor who was holding on to him and for some strange reason felt compelled to introduce himself, he held out his hand and said.

"Good evening, Drought's the name, Charles Drought, senior third engineer, I am pleased to meet you."

The young sailor burst out laughing and shook Charles hand, "Are all you scousers on the 'Conveyor' comedians?"

"Why do you say that?"

"Just before you came aboard we hoisted a survivor on deck, his survival suit was full of water from the waist down, it had not been put on properly, we had to lay him down on the deck and cut his suit away from him and while we were doing that he said "I didn't see this advertised in the Cunard Cruise Brochure", would you believe it?, what a comedian he was, he said he was your second engineer".

"I would believe it, that's Graham Ross, nothing ever fazes him, but I am concerned about the Chief Engineer. He was the last to leave my raft he should be right behind me will you look out for him and get him aboard safely."

"Don't you worry about your Chief, sir, we'll get him safely on board now let's get you down below and out of all your gear, you must be frozen half to death."

Another sailor took him by the arm and gently led him to a doorway in an alleyway and down a flight of steps, there were people waiting at the bottom of the steps for any survivors arriving. One sailor approached Charles "Let me help you to get all your gear off" he said kindly.

"Sure go ahead, I think I'll need all the help I can get, my hands and fingers are stiff with the cold."

"I can see that and you are shaking like a flag in the wind but that will probably be from shock after the trauma you have just been through."

With his help Charles removed his survival suit and his life jacket, the sailor noticed that Charles was wearing his gas mask case, he took hold of it and gave a disapproving look at Charles.

"You shouldn't have been wearing this you know sir, that could have weighed you down and drowned you."

"I had to, its got my identity card, a cheque book and a bankers card all wrapped up in a plastic bag, it is the only means of identification I have got if I was found floating arse up in the sea. The MoD in their wonderful wisdom, deemed it not necessary to issue us Merchant Navy blokes with identification tags like they dished out to all the Military and Naval bods, they deemed a lot of things not necessary for us poor buggers" said Charles. The fact that the MoD did not think it was necessary to put mortars on board the 'Conveyor' to fire "Chaff" to protect them from an aerial attack by "Exocets" still rankled him immensely.

"Sorry sir, point taken, I will take you to the Ratings Mess deck now so you can get changed into warmer and drier clothes."

He led Charles along an alleyway towards a large room, a Naval officer was seated at a table outside the entrance of the Mess Room.

" I will leave you here and get back to my station to help any other survivors. Good Luck".

With a wave of his hand and a smile at Charles, he walked away, back to his station.

"Thanks for all your help and consideration" shouted Charles after him.

"Be my guest" he shouted back.

"Right sir, are you ready now?" asked the Naval officer at the desk.

"Yes, what do you want to know?"

"May I have your name, home address and next of kin?"

"What's all that for?" queried Charles.

"We need all this information for the identification of the survivors in order to relay it to Cunard and the MOD" he answered, and he wrote all the details Charles gave him down on a large list.

"Thank you, you can go in now sir and join the other survivors."

Charles's shivering spell had passed over and he moved into a large room, furnished with tables and benches, the room was full of survivors, all from the 'Conveyor', in various stages of undress, all in the process of changing into dry clothes which they were picking out of big cardboard boxes. He looked around the room trying to pick out familiar faces. In a corner in the rear of the room he saw Graham, the second engineer, stripping off to change into dry gear, he quickly crossed the room towards him.

"Hey! Graham, boy am I glad to see you made it safely off the 'Conveyor' Charles slapped him on the back.

"I'm glad I made it too, it was pretty hairy on the ship, there were times when I didn't think I was going to make it but it's great to see you all in one piece Charles."

"I had my moments when I thought I was going to ring 'finished with engines' they both laughed at Charles's phraseology, "How did you get off the 'Conveyor' Graham I didn't see much of you after we left the safety room?"

"I think I was about one of the last to leave her, I just climbed over the side on to the nearest ladder, it was slow going with the ship rolling all over the place, as I got further down I could see that the bottom half of the ladder was all smashed and was burning away"

"It was the 'Alacrity' that smashed the ladders trying to get alongside us and off load us all directly from ship to ship but they had to back off as the weather conditions worsened" interrupted Charles.

"And a right botched up job they made of it" said Graham morosely.

"Any way you are here Graham carry on what you were telling me."

"Oh yes, where was I up to?"

"You were saying you had seen the ladder burnt and smashed beneath you."

"Right, well I had no other alternative to get off the ship but to make a jump for it into the sea and that idea didn't fill me with a great deal of confidence I can tell you, talk about 'out of the frying pan into the fire'. I swam over to the nearest liferaft, but was told that 'it was full' and was left with no alternative but to swim around in the freezing water until helped into another liferaft by a more accommodating occupant, so here I am" Graham concluded with outstretched arms.

"Well done Graham," a very pleased Charles replied "But did you see anything of the 'Old Man'? I did not see anything of him at all on board and he certainly isn't in this room."

"Yes, I did but only briefly, I was too busy trying to save my own skin, I saw Captain North was on the bridge. Old 'Birdseye' is one of the old school of Masters on ships, not the new type that shouts ' Abandon ship, women and children first, follow me' oh no, he knew his duty and his commitments to his crew. He had got his priorities right, to oversee the safe evacuation of all of us first, and then himself. That Naval chap Captain Layard, the boss of all his own mob of Royal Navy guys on board, well he was up there standing alongside the 'Old Man' all the time."

"Good for him, I remember him alright" Charles said with a smile.

"The next time I saw the Captain he was in the sea clinging to the grab lines of an overcrowded raft, the raft had been cut free by one of those divers who were swimming about helping the survivors.

The increasing wind and swell was pushing the raft towards the stern of the ship and suddenly it disappeared under the pitching stern, the raft re-emerged from the pounding of the stern but it was half empty."

Graham hesitated briefly finding it hard to recall that tragic moment, he looked away from Charles and gave a little cough to clear his throat and swallowed hard. He returned his gaze upon Charles "I never saw him again Charles."

They both remained silent looking at each other, shaking their heads in disbelief and in sadness that they had lost their Captain, a brave and conscientious man, a man they admired and respected so much as a human being and a seaman of the highest order.

"It doesn't seem fair does it Graham to lose the 'old man' after all he did for us and his ship?" said a very sad Charles.

"No it doesn't Charles it's hard to understand why these things happen."

Their solemn thoughts were broken into when over the ships Public Address system a voice announced. "All survivors of the "Atlantic Conveyor" welcome aboard. Please avail yourselves of the refreshments available and make sure that you obtain a survival pack and change into dry clothes. Please do not worry, be calm, you are safe now."

Charles turned to Graham "They seem pretty bloody sure we are safe now, how can they tell? Just because we are on a Naval vessel and why is it all these navy bods talk so 'la de da'?"

"They have got to otherwise no promotion for them" they both laughed at this observation. "Lets get our survival packages and grab a mug of tea or whatever, I heard once that the Navy was big into cocoa or "Ka" as they called it."

"Right ho Charles, lead the way."

They walked over to the tables that held all the survival packages and there they met the Chief and Bill, his assistant on watch.

"You made it Chief and you Bill, but it was a close thing though wasn't it?"

"You are bloody right it was a close thing, I don't ever want to go through that lot ever again in my life" the Chief replied.

Charles turned to Bill who looked tired and drawn "You are soaking wet Bill, let me help you change into all this dry gear in these packs."

"Thanks Charles."

"You look very worried Bill, what's your problem?"

"Firstly where are we going to sleep and secondly my back is aching like all hell, when I was in Liverpool I thought I shouldn't be signing on so soon after my major operation on my spine and now I bloody well know I shouldn't have come on this trip."

"Never mind, think of the money you have earned" Charles jokingly tried to lift Bill's spirits.

"Sod the money" he gruffly replied, and they both laughed together.

They sat together at a small table sipping their mugs of tea, they were all tired, cold and still a little bit frightened after their experiences and feeling thoroughly depressed and miserable.

"Charles would you do me a favour?" asked Bill.

"Sure anything."

He passed three very soggy ten pound notes to Charles. "Will you look after this for me? you will probably get better accommodation than me and have a better opportunity to look after money."

"No problem Bill, it will be safe with me, and it's good ale money when we get back ashore."

"We'll spend the lot together Charles" he happily replied, his spirits for the moment somewhat lifted with the prospect of a good night out ashore.

An announcement came over the Public Address system that anyone who thought he did not need the survival pack to hand them back, as there were not enough for everyone. Charles did not think he was that wet and was contemplating returning his pack when he was taken by another quite uncontrollable attack of shivering, he could not help himself, his teeth were chattering and the whole of his body started shaking badly. They were all alarmed at the sudden change, the Chief immediately recognised the symptoms of traumatic shock and was first to react.

"Go and try and find a medical officer as quick as you can" he ordered Bill "and Graham get more hot tea and put enough sugar in it that you can stand a spoon up in it."

"On my way Chief."

The Chief took hold of Charles's trembling body and hugged him close to his chest trying to impart some warmth into it, another person seeing the situation threw a blanket over them.

"I can't find a medical officer anywhere" Bill said on his return.

"It's the same everywhere, you can never find a bloody policeman when you want one, don't worry Bill, he's going to be OK."

"Here is the tea Chief, how is he?" a concerned Graham asked.

"We'll get this tea down him and that should steady him up a bit."

The Chief held the mug to Charles's lips and he was able to sip it gently and with each sip his trembling became less and less. The attack did not last too long much to the relief of all concerned and it slowly passed over leaving Charles in a lather of cold sweat.

Another announcement came over the Public Address system "Gentlemen, please listen carefully to the following instructions. Will all officers proceed to the wardroom Petty Officers to the Petty Officers' wardroom and all ratings remain were they are. Thank you."

The Chief bent over Charles "Will you be OK to get to the wardroom under your own steam or do you need any help."

"Help like what?"

"A wheel chair, if they have got such a thing on board here"

"Christ no, I am not that bad, just let me lean on you Chief."

They stood up, Charles's legs were still quivering slightly and he felt very cold, and with the help of the Chief he made his way to the wardroom, being guided by one of the Naval ratings.

Charles stood in the doorway, surveying a very crowded wardroom when a young Naval officer approached him.

"I say old chap, you look a bit groggy let me find you a seat" he took Charles from the arm of the Chief and gently ushered him across the Ward Room to a chair in the corner.

"Can I get you anything to drink?" he asked kindly and before Charles could thank him a voice said "It's all right, I'll look after Charles now."

Charles looked up and saw an Army Lieutenant standing in front of him, he did not recognise him at first and then it slowly dawned on him it was the young man he had struck up a good relationship with on the 'Conveyor'. They used to have pre-lunch drinks every day and sit together to have their lunch.

"Fancy meeting you here" exclaimed Charles.

"We chaps are everywhere" he replied with a sly smile. Charles remembered someone had once told him that he was a member of the elite SAS group. "Look here Charles, you are wet through, I'll go and get some dry gear for you, sit tight and don't move" and he hurried away.

Charles had not appreciated the fact that he was soaking wet just as though he had been in the sea. The Lieutenant returned in no time at all and immediately started to help Charles strip off all his wet clothes and change into the dry navy issue.

"What do the Navy make their underwear out of bloody sandpaper?" complained Charles. "These trousers are too small and the shirt too big, I must look a real clown in this rig, but at least the shoes and socks fit quite well."

"Hey, beggars can't be chooses" the Lieutenant laughingly replied.

"Thanks a lot, now I am drier and warmer I feel much better, I do appreciate your help" a grateful Charles said to him.

"I am only too delighted to help you in some little way, I was always appreciative of the privilege you accorded to me by allowing me to use your cabin, when you were on watch down in the engine room so that I could have a little privacy to write to my wife back at home. You can appreciate there is not a lot of privacy when you are crammed four or more in a cabin built for one. This is my small way of saying thank you for all your kindness."

"I only let you use my cabin because you always left it tidier than it was when I left it."

"I don't believe that for one moment" and he smiled at Charles.

"I am still a bit disorientated and unsure where I am. What's the name of this ship?" asked Charles.

"You are on board 'HMS Alacrity', a Naval Frigate, and you are sitting in the officers' wardroom; it acts as a dining room and a lounge for the officers" explained the Lieutenant.

Charles looked slowly around the wardroom still not sure of his surroundings. He could see a sort of mock fireplace and fender at one end of the room that had a carpet in front of it. On the main bulkhead was a picture of the Queen and next to her Prince Philip in full Naval uniform, elsewhere other pictures depicted high ranking Naval officers and Naval ships.

"A nice cosy place they have here" remarked Charles.

"Yes it's not bad for a little frigate."

Naval ratings arrived in the wardroom with folding camp beds and blankets and the survivors were asked to collect a camp bed and some blankets, and find somewhere in the wardroom as a sleeping quarter.

"No need for you to bother about a camp bed Charles, I have fixed it up with the Navigating Officer who is acting as the temporary Accommodation Officer, and you will have a place on the wardroom settee in the bar area, what do you think about that?" he announced grandly.

"That's great it will be the first time in my life I have been officially told I can stop in the bar all night."

"Well Charles, I think I have done all I can for you, I must return to my other duties now, it has been a great pleasure meeting you and sharing your friendship. I hope some day we may meet again in more pleasant surroundings and circumstances, good bye and good luck" he shook Charles warmly by the hand and left him.

Charles watched him walk all the way across the wardroom and disappear through the doorway.

"Now that's one hell of a nice chap" Charles said to himself "I don't suppose we will ever meet again."

His thoughts were interrupted by the unmistakable voice of the Chief.

"How are you feeling now Charles? You are beginning to look more like your old self again."

"I'm feeling a lot better thank you Chief, very tired though."

"Have you got yourself fixed up for somewhere to sleep?"

Yes, that army Lieutenant I used to have drinks with on the 'Conveyor' and let him use my room to write letters home got me a bunk on a settee in the bar area."

"You lucky sod, you always fall on your feet, he must have had some pull to fix you up there, what was his name?" a curious Chief asked.

"You know Chief that was the strange part of our friendship, he never told me his name, I did ask him once and all he said was "Just call me Lieutenant" I believe he was something to do with the SAS."

"Very secretive and cagey those SAS blokes, you don't get much out of them" the Chief said nodding sagely.

"I suppose they have to be, shame really, he has done a hell of a lot for me on here I would have liked to have met up with him again ashore and bought him a drink or two."

The Public Address system interrupted their conversation by inviting all who wished to do so, to go on deck and look at the 'Conveyor', which was still burning, for the last time.

"I don't think I can bring myself to do that Chief, I feel bad enough having to abandon her, let alone seeing her in her last death throes, I want to remember her in her prime."

"I understand Charles, I'll just pop up and say goodbye to the 'old girl' for both of us."

"Go ahead Chief, I'll wait here for you."

The Chief returned looking rather subdued. "I wish I hadn't gone on deck to see her after all, you were very wise to stay below Charles, it was quite a spectacular sight, all that smoke and flames shooting out from her everywhere, but in retrospect it was a sight I would have rather missed" he sighed deeply.

Seafarers, although they always complain about something on the various ships they sail on, they do get very attached to them and regard them as their home, like people ashore regard their houses as their home. They feel particularly sad when they hear of a ship they had sailed on and carried fond memories of, had been lost at sea. It was that strange relationship that seafarers develop between themselves, the sea, and a ship, and is hard to explain.

"Ah well Charles I'm off to my bunk, I've managed to get a cosy spot, not as cosy as yours though" he said with a smile.

"Me too Chief, Good night."

Charles walked a little unsteadily to the settee in the bar, still a bit weak from all that had happened to him. He quickly slipped out of his shoes and trousers, lay down on the settee and pulled the blanket over himself. At first he found it impossible to get to sleep, his mind racing, thinking about the 'Conveyor' and the men from her who had not yet been accounted for. Eventually he fell into a fitful sleep, but he was frequently disturbed, for some reason the ship's air conditioning had not been switched off, and he kept waking up from the perishing cold. On a few occasions when he was awake from the cold he heard the sound of machine gun fire, this did little for his peace of mind.

There was a small pantry area on the same deck as the wardroom and it was manned throughout the night by two Royal Navy Stewards who very obligingly dispensed tea, coffee, cocoa and sandwiches by request. Charles availed himself of these facilities during the long, cold and unsettling night. He asked one of the stewards what all the machine gun fire was about that he kept hearing from time to time and was told that the ship was patrolling the Falkland Sound and the machine gunning was sinking any empty life rafts they came cross, so as not to be mistaken for any rafts still containing survivors.

Charles could hear a radio in the wardroom, which was tuned to the B.B.C. World Service, giving out hourly bulletins on the situation in the Falklands campaign. On his last visit to the pantry he heard the announcement that the 'Atlantic Conveyor' had been hit by an Exocet missile, set on fire and abandoned, and that there was no report of survivors.

"Dear Lord, I hope and pray these bulletins are not being broadcast on the home service, it will cause all kinds of alarm and anxiety back home" Charles said to himself. He lay down again on the settee and fell into a deep sleep even though his mind was so greatly troubled.

The next day, the crew members of the 'Alacrity' kindly gave all of the survivors one of their precious aerogrammes, so that all could write home to their loved ones to let them know that they had survived the ordeal of being sunk.

15

THOSE WHO WAIT AND WEEP

The Reverend Canon Robert "Bob" Evans is a man beloved by Merchant Seamen and their families throughout Merseyside, and by all those seafarers who arrive in the Port of Liverpool. He is truly a man of God and a man for all the Christian needs of those who go down to the sea in ships. He has been the Chaplain at his waterfront 'vicarage' at Kingston House with its world wide famous symbol of the 'Flying Angel' for over 35 years. His parish covers 2,000 acres of land and water, were some of his flock have their homes on oil tankers, cargo ships and tug boats. He has a great affinity with the Liverpool Pilot Service and is the Honorary Chaplain of the Anchorage Club, a club established for retired seafaring officers.

Reverend Bob is one the main connections for comforting between those at sea and their loved ones at home, his telephone is rarely silent, it often rings at all hours of the day and night and such is his dedication it never goes unanswered. No-one is more aware than he of the urgency behind those ringing tones, he knows a comforting word or message from him can make a world of difference to those anxious calls about their men away at sea.

When he heard that the 'Atlantic Conveyor' had sailed from Liverpool for the Falklands he knew there would be seafarers from Merseyside who would have volunteered to serve with the task force at the other end of the world, sailing aboard her. He immediately contacted the head office of Cunard and requested a full crew list of all on board her, from this list he picked out the men and their addresses who were from his parish and the surrounding parishes on Merseyside. He then contacted every vicar who had a crewmember in his parish and informed them that one or more of his parishioners were sailing on the 'Atlantic Conveyor' into the Falklands conflict.

Reverend Canon Bob Evans

With the Falklands situation as it was, deep down inside of him he knew there was a real possibility he would have to break the news of any casualties or deaths to the wives or parents in his parish. Bob had a philosophy that seafarers are very professional and often take risks, the sea is a massive untamed space and any ship no matter how large is relatively very small in it, he knows they have seen those risks probably many times generally from the terrifying strength of a storm lashed sea. The hardest and toughest task for him, which he has had to do on a number of occasions in his 35 years of chaplaincy, was to break the news of a bereavement and he never ceased to wonder at the courage of the people involved on hearing such news.

One of the strangest things about death at sea, although the news is given, there is no funeral. A funeral is a focal point, after which those who mourned can get on with their lives but in the case of the next of kin of a man lost at sea it seems that the voyage is still going on. There is an element of disbelief at what has happened and in some cases it is a long and agonising time before the reality of it all strikes home.

Liverpool is like a village, there is hardly a family without some seafaring connection and when someone is lost at sea the whole community is lessened by it. When he heard that the 'Atlantic Conveyor' had become a victim of the fighting in the Falklands, the first information he received was from the M.o.D. It was very brief ,he was told the ship had been hit by an Exocet, set on fire, and had to be abandoned and as rescue operations were still continuing they could give no accurate news of casualties.

His telephone rang incessantly, with wives and relatives frantically seeking information about their loved ones, there were plenty of tears but there was little he could tell them other than what he had heard from the M.o.D. There was no information coming from Cunard but Bob talked to them offering comfort and hope to try and overcome their fears. Fortunately, what he thought was going to be a sad and difficult task of contacting families with the news they had lost a loved one, turned into immense relief after contacting Cunard and was told the men from his parish had all survived but had no information of their condition. He joyfully passed this good news on to all the wives and parents who were anxiously waiting and to the vicars in the other parishes. The tears of grief and worry became tears of joy and exaltation when they received the glad tidings from Bob that their men were safe. Unfortunately it was not all good news for those who waited and wept in other parishes up and down the country.

Mrs. Winifred Garvey had been anxiously waiting at her home in Bootle from the time Bob had told her the 'Atlantic Conveyor' had been set on fire and abandoned, never daring to leave the house for one second in case she missed an all important message that her husband John (45 years.) a GP1 was a survivor and if he was injured in any way. The Garvey family were no strangers to the worry and stress of war, they knew only too well the feelings of fear and tension waiting to hear about their men at war at sea. Mrs. Garvey had both her father and grandfather torpedoed and captured by the Germans in WW 2. She had tried to persuade him not to go but he had volunteered straight away and nothing would deter him, that was the typical attitude of every Liverpool seaman whenever war broke out. It was a tremendous sense of relief in the Garvey household when Reverend Bob imparted the glad news to them, Mrs.Garvey's reply to Bob on hearing the news was simply but heartfelt "There is a God in Heaven Padre I will never doubt that".

Charles Drought's wife Betty, was out visiting a neighbours' sick child in Arrowe Park hospital when the news broke that the 'Atlantic Conveyor' had been abandoned and was on fire. Soon after returning home their vicar visited her thanks to Canon Bob's foresight and told her what had happened. Deeply shocked she could not stop shaking, all her fears and premonitions of what could happen to Charles had been realised.

16

ROLL CALL

At last Charles's restless night was over, he quickly visited the bathroom and went for his breakfast. He surprised himself by eating a really hearty meal feeling well sated he returned to the wardroom. A Naval officer approached him immediately he entered.

"Excuse me sir, would you please attend a roll call in the crews mess room for all the survivors from the 'Atlantic Conveyor?' he requested.

"Sure will."

"You know the way to the crews mess room do you sir?"

"Yes, I was in there when I first came on board."

He entered the mess room and walked over to stand with the other engineers and nodded a good morning to them all. A distinguished Naval Officer took the roll call and then informed them that twelve of their shipmates were not accounted for. They were told the main body of the survivors were aboard the 'Alacrity' other survivors had been picked up by 'HMS Brilliant' and the two Aircraft Carriers 'HMS Hermes' and 'Invincible'."

"I did not realise we had lost as many as twelve of our crew, I was praying that at least most of those who were missing might yet turn up" said Charles sadly, to no one in particular.

"I don't think your prayers were answered though" someone said.

"No I'm afraid not".

When the roll call was over, Captain Layard, the Royal Naval Captain on the 'Atlantic Conveyor', stood up and addressed the assembled survivors.

"Gentlemen, no doubt some of you or maybe all of you are still very bemused about what had happened and how it had happened even why it had happened. I will try, very briefly, to cover all the facts that led to the attack on the 'Conveyor'. May 25th, the day we were hit, was Argentines National Day, we knew the Latin American temperament would not let this day pass without some spectacular strike and we had been forewarned to be extra vigilant for any air strikes.

On May 25th Argentine reconnaissance located a very large ship with the British Task Force approaching the Falkland Sound and they believed it to be one of the two Aircraft Carriers they had been waiting for to come within range of their aircraft to justify using one or two of their few remaining Exocets. As you know the Carriers had been kept well to the east of the Falklands to keep out of the range of the missiles".

The Captain paused "I am not boring you am I?" he asked "Do you want me to carry on?" There was a unanimous yes from everyone in the room they were completely enthralled listening to the Captain unfold the story of the "Conveyors" destruction.

"Right ho then, well, with the naval air battle showing no lessening of intensity, the Argies assumed a 'Carrier' had been drawn towards the Falkland Sound and into their range, and if it could be disabled or sunk, the odds on the daily battle at San Carlos would again be in their favour.

Their assumption was wrong, the large ship was the 'Conveyor' and not the much desired Aircraft Carrier. Two French built Super Etendards were immediately scrambled and armed with their precious Exocets and were despatched from a mainland air base, using the same tactic of flying-low, that was so successful in sinking 'HMS Sheffield', to avoid radar detection. They made a long sweep south of the Falklands before making a tight turn north towards the Task Force and what they thought was an Aircraft Carrier. When twenty miles from their intended target they released their highly prized and irreplaceable deadly sea skimming Excocet missiles believing their target was none other than 'HMS Hermes', instead confused by similar radar profiles they were heading for the 'Conveyor'.

This error has reduced the number of these deadly weapons held by the Argentine Air Force to one, but that's not much of a consolation to us is it?" The Captain took a sip of his tea from the mug that had been brought to him "It's dry work all this talking" he said with a smile "I wish it was something stronger". Putting the mug down on the table in front of him, he carried on with his story.

"The Royal Navy has a code word for everything, it's the way they work, and the code word for an oncoming Exocet attack was "Ashtray", don't ask me why? At 1536hrs the dreaded code word was relayed to all ships in the Task Force. They all immediately began firing off their Chaff rockets and successfully diverted the two Exocets away from themselves but as we were not fitted with Chaff rockets the two Exocets locked on to the large profile of the 'Conveyor', we could do nothing to avoid them and we were struck on the port side aft, in the vicinity of the engine room, the rest you all know."

"Why in hell's name didn't they fit us with Chaff rockets" an angry voice shouted out. Before Captain Layard could answer someone shouted back. "I can tell you why it was because the bloody MoD said it was too expensive" "I really don't know about that" the Captain replied "but I do know they had planned for helicopters to play a vital role against these deadly Exocets by acting as decoys."

"How would that work?" came another question.

"The idea was that the Exocets radar would lock on to the helicopter instead of its intended target, a ship, the 'copter' would be hovering about 27feet, even less at times, above the sea, the missiles flight path came in at that height and at the very last moment the 'copter' would shoot up above this height and the Exocet would pass harmlessly away underneath them, they hoped. Daring, but a very deadly and dangerous manoeuvre."

"Where the hell were the helicopters when we were hit?" he was asked. "Unfortunately I can't answer that question because I do not know but if it's any consolation to you all, if the Exocets had struck us an hour earlier when most of our men were on 'B' and 'C' decks I can tell you the death toll would have been higher considerably higher". He looked around the room and was silent for a few moments.

"Any more questions Gentlemen?" The room remained silent, they were all meditating on what they had just heard.

"Well Gentlemen, that is all that I have managed to glean from my superiors, you now know as much as I do, there are many questions left unanswered I am sure but as the French would say 'C'est la.guerre'. We have a good working relationship here and I am sad and angry we were not able to complete our allotted task and land all our equipment. You are not gladiators, you are not trained for war, you are not trained to kill but you all adapted to the rigours of wartime service with commendable ease. The shipmates who died bravely, doing their duty, was in the best tradition that is renowned in the Merchant Navy in wartime. In times of war you have never been known to shirk your duty and let your country down and you all have kept that wonderful tradition of loyalty today. I am full of admiration for you all and it has been a great privilege to serve with such men as you".

He paused for a moment and took a deep breath "That is all I have to say I bid you good day, and may God be with you as you journey safely home to your loved ones". He smartly saluted the assembled company and walked out of the mess room. They all remained quiet for some time taking in all that had been said to them, Charles broke the silence by talking to Graham, the second engineer, and soon everyone was chattering away.

"You know what Graham? The most annoying thing about all this, is that it all could have been avoided but for the penny pinchers at the MoD who wouldn't put the mortars on board to fire the "Chaff" rockets, that is what really sickens me"

"It sickens me also Charles, I bet those dumb clowns of civil servants at the MoD couldn't care less what's happened to us but that's all in the past now and we mustn't linger on it, it could destroy us" a bitter Graham said.

"You are right Graham, what's done is done and the only way to forget it is to go 'Full Ahead'. Let's see if the ship's NAFFI shop is open, I need a toothbrush, shaving gear, and a comb and some decent underwear not made with sand paper". They both laughed at this observation.

" How are we going to pay for all this stuff" enquired Graham.

"No problem, Bill my mechanic, gave me thirty quid to look after for him. He thought it would be safer with me, we can use some of that and I can square it with him on pay day."

They entered the NAFFI and saw Bill standing at a counter "Hello Bill doing some shopping?" greeted Charles.

"Am I glad to see you," replied Bill " I haven't a bean on me and I need a toothbrush, tooth paste, shaving cream, you name it; I need it."

"You are in the same boat as us Bill, we need all those things."

"Have you got that thirty quid on you that I lent you for safe keeping?"

"No, I spent it all on ale in the bar."

"You did what?" exclaimed an astonished Bill.

"No, only joking, here it is all intact" Charles handed a somewhat crumpled three ten pound notes to Bill.

"OK then, let's go and stock up, the tabs on me."

All three made their much needed purchases and just in time, they bought the last three toothbrushes the NAFFI had. On their return to the wardroom a ship's officer was waiting to give them ten pounds each.

"This should cover you for any essential purchases you wish to make or have made" he said eyeing the toiletries they had in their hands.

"Thank you very much" Charles said "but how do we repay this ten pounds to the Navy?"

The officer gave Charles an old fashioned look "Well all I can say sir, if they ask for the money back there is no God in heaven" and he walked away to give out the money to other survivors in the room.

During lunch Charles was approached by a Naval officer. "Excuse me sir I hope you do not mind me interrupting your lunch, but with the Captain's compliments, he would like you to represent your engine room staff at the burial party at 1500hrs this afternoon, we are committing three of your crew from the 'Atlantic Conveyor' to the sea and he wishes you to assist with the actual committal,"

"Yes of course I will" Charles instantly replied "and will you give the Captain my compliments and thank him for asking me to participate in the service, I appreciate it very much."

"I most certainly will sir, and thank you."

It was a very cold, bleak grey afternoon with a heavy swell and a choppy sea, Charles stood at the head of the board that had the Merchant Navy flag draped over the body of Frank Foulkes, one of the engineer mechanics, two Royal Navy officers stood at the head of the boards draped in the Royal Navy ensign and the Union Jack, this was for one of the Chinese crew who came from Hong Kong. The 'Alacrity' Captain, Captain Craig conducted the service with due reverence as befitting so sad an occasion. At a sign from the Captain Charles raised his board, in unison with the other two, and Frank Foulke's body was committed to the cold and relentless sea. Charles was deeply moved, it seemed such a desolate part of the ocean, no marker where he lay and so far away from his beloved home in England. After the service they all gathered around the bar, a little subdued but the Captain had ordered that all the drinks be charged to him.

"That's a nice gesture from the Captain to enable us to send off Frank in good Merchant Navy style, but I tell you what, I never ever wish to have to partake in such a ceremony again. God forbid that the same situation should ever arise again" announced Charles. They all nodded in total agreement.

After dinner the old problem of where they were going to sleep came up again. The accommodation officer came to Charles "Were you comfortable last night in the bar area?" he asked.

"Like hell I was, it was bloody freezing, some idiot had messed up the air conditioning."

"Oh! Right ho then, we will have to re-allocate you, just hang on a minute I will go and see what I can do."

The influence of the Army Lieutenant seemed to still prevail on board ,much to Charles's delight. After a while the officer returned looking very pleased with himself.

"I have got you reallocated to an electrical contactor room" he proudly told Charles "it is a bit cramped, you will be sharing it with someone else but at least it will be warmer. I have put your camp bed and blanket in there."

Charles sent a silent prayer of thanks for the Army Lieutenant whom he had befriended on board the 'Conveyor'. Charles was led to a small room not far from the wardroom and found Neil McGowan, the 'Conveyor's' electrical officer, making up his camp bed.

"Hello Neil, it looks like we are going to be bunk mates tonight."

"Aye that we are, I hope you don't snore?"

"Strange that, I was just going to ask you the same question" he laughingly replied. Charles's anticipation of a good night's rest, warm and without any disturbances never materialised, a series of electrical clicks at frequent intervals from a panel right along side his head prevented any hope of an unbroken sleep. The night became another dreadfully long drawn out night, he felt he was fated never ever to get a good night's sleep again and Charles could hardly wait for the dawn to break.

When Charles entered the wardroom for breakfast next morning, he could not help but feel there was more than the usual chit-chat going around.

"What's everybody so excited about?" he asked.

"You haven't heard then?"

"I haven't heard a damn thing, I have just got out of my bunk after a bloody awful night's sleep" was his querulous reply.

"Why was that, did Neil snore all night?" they all burst out laughing. Charles could see that all the tension had gone out of them, there was a different atmosphere all together.

"You guys are really on a high, what's the news?"

"There is some speculation about us being taken off from here tonight under the cover of darkness and there is a rumour doing the rounds we will be going home on the QEII" was the reply.

The thought of going home to Betty, a warm bed, a good night's sleep and all the comforts of a tranquil home life away from the stress and strain he had suffered over the last few days and the misery of two sleepless nights, lifted his spirits enormously, even the constant pain in his shoulder seem to disappear, it was a tremendous feeling. For the first time in over 48 hours he felt a warm glow of happiness inside him.

"That is great news" an elated Charles said " I don't care if we go home on a clapped out, coal burning tramp ship with no food, as long as we get home."

"I wonder why the powers to be want us home as quickly as possible?" the Chief remarked.

"I can tell you the answer to that question Chief, its Cunard, they don't want to pay us all this money, plus the war bonuses, for just sitting around on our backsides doing nothing, even after what we have been through" concluded Charles.

"You could be right there Charles" laughed the Chief.

Charles spent the next few hours happily being given a guided tour, with six others, of the 'Alacrity' by the officers who were most considerate and hospitable at all times. Charles was most impressed with the engine room, quite small with so much equipment and so many people attending to various jobs, he smiled as he said to himself "We have an engine room on the 'Conveyor' twice as big as this and man it with three people, four at the most."

They arrived back to the wardroom "Anyone for a drink, I am gasping after all that trailing around the ship?" asked Charles. Before anyone could answer the Public Address system announced "Will all the survivors from the 'Atlantic Conveyor' be prepared to disembark by helicopter at once."

No-one wanted a second bidding, especially Charles, with all thoughts of a drink gone, he quickly threw his few belongings into a paper bag he had been given. He dressed himself in his survival suit and life jacket and waited expectantly for the next orders.

17

LIFT OFF

When everyone had returned to the wardroom suitably kitted up in their survival suits and life jackets, they were told that the Wessex V and the Sea King helicopters were too large to land on deck and therefore they would be hoisted up by winch whilst the helicopter hovered about twenty feet above the deck.

"I don't think much of this idea of getting off the ship" moaned Charles who was always afraid of any heights.

"Hard luck, but it's the only way we are going to get off this ship" someone said.

Luckily one of the 'Conveyor' survivors in the party was himself a Naval helicopter Pilot. "Listen to me you chaps" he said in a commanding voice "It's no problem being winched up, I will show you how to fasten yourself into a winch strap" he held a strap up for all to see " there will be someone there to help you anyway, and I will tell you how to position yourself whilst being hoisted up". He probably had the most attentive audience in his life as he went through the procedures of being hoisted up, everyone stared intently at his demonstration and hung on to his every word.

Charles was not totally convinced he would be safely hauled aboard the helicopter even after that demonstration.

The weather had improved a little, but the ship was still rolling about, and the sea and sky was still grey and forbidding.

"Right ho Chaps" a voice called out "in your groups get in a single file and make your way down to the Flight Deck."

Charles was allocated to a group containing mainly engine room staff. As he moved off he suddenly looked around.

"Where's the Chief? Why isn't he with us?" Charles said in a concerned voice.

"I'm here Charles, don't get your knickers in a twist, I will be joining you later"

"Why's that?" a still very concerned Charles wanted to know.

"I have been selected to go by a chopper, with a few others, and if possible land on what's left of the 'Conveyor'. She is still afloat I am told, and I will generally assess the situation to see whether any of her precious cargo is perhaps undamaged and therefore able to be salvaged". He spoke very calmly and without a trace of nervousness considering the danger this task posed, landing on a burning hulk still full of explosives.

"Jesus Christ Chief, it will be impossible to salvage anything on her. You know as well as I do she was a roaring inferno throughout, ready to go up at anytime, nothing could survive in that blaze" a shocked Charles reminded the Chief.

"I know Charles, but orders are orders, what did Kipling say 'We are not to question why, just do it and die' or something like that."

"Sod Kipling and his exceedingly good cakes" Charles replied, they smiled at each other both recalling a well know advert on T.V. at that time.

Before Charles could say any more he was ordered to the Flight Deck with his party, but not before he shook hands with the Chief "You look after number one at all times Chief, I want to see you back safely" The Chief just nodded and walked away.

Charles stood on the Flight Deck for a while and eventually a helicopter appeared and hovered above him. The noise was so tremendous from the roar of the helicopters rotors that none of his party could converse with one another. He watched in trepidation as one by one his party was winched up into the aircraft. He thought to himself "This must be what it is like waiting to be hung". He was concerned about the small paper bag containing all his worldly possessions that he was clutching tightly in his hand but as he moved forward towards his lift off position they were taken from him and he was told they would be delivered to him later. He was led beneath the roaring helicopter, the winch man slipped the harness over him and pulled it tight to his chest he pulled his arms down straight to his sides. With a cheery smile and a pat on the back he gave a thumbs up sign and Charles was whisked into the air.

He stared straight ahead of him, too frightened to look down or anywhere else for that matter. His ascent stopped abruptly and he spun round and found he was facing the doorway of the helicopter. A crewman was standing in the doorway, he reached out and grabbed Charles by the shoulder. Charles let out a shout of pain but no-one could hear him above the noise of the helicopters rotors. He was spun round with his back to the door and drawn towards the doorway, Charles felt the back of his knees make contact with the door sill and he was promptly pushed down into a sitting position. He was quickly released from his harness and drawn inside the aircraft and assisted to a seat on the left hand side of the aircraft right behind the co-pilot.

Charles slumped down in his seat and heaved a big sigh of relief that another hair raising episode was safely over. "I wonder how many more traumas I am going to have to go through before I get the hell out of this godforsaken place" he mused to himself. He looked up and found he was sitting opposite Keith, the fourth engineer.

"Fancy meeting you here..." he suddenly stopped speaking realising it was useless to talk above all the noise, he just smiled at Keith and gave the thumbs up sign and mouthed 'OK'.

Keith returned the greeting in the same fashion and pointed at the co-pilot mouthing words but Charles could not make out what he was trying to say. Charles looked at the back of the co-pilot and all he could see was a flying helmet and his shoulders with epaulettes. He nodded back to Keith as if he understood what he was saying.

The helicopter trip was a completely new experience for Charles. He enjoyed the unusual flight but found it a terribly noisy way to travel and he tried to see as much as he could outside by looking through the open side door of the 'copter'. He did see the odd ship as they passed over it but mainly it was the grey, forbidding sea with the addition of white wave caps and he knew there was quite a wind blowing. "That's all I bloody well need, a howling gale trying to get off this 'chopper'" he groaned inwardly. The helicopter did a lot of swaying and turning about which did nothing to help Charles dispel his fears of height, it only increased it, he had no idea where he was being taken to as for some reason the Naval personnel had omitted to tell him.

After about fifteen minutes the helicopter steadied itself, the winch man got out of his little folding seat and beckoned to Charles.

"Oh my God, here we go again, why must I be the first to go?" moaned Charles to himself, swallowing hard. With much trepidation he unclipped himself from his seat and was guided to the open door of the helicopter, by gesticulation the winch man conveyed to Charles that he wanted him to sit down and he then placed a strap round and under his arms. The winch hoist gently lifted him to a semi-sitting position and walking on his heels he put his feet over the door sill and sat down with his feet dangling in space. The noise of the rotors was deafening and the wind was howling around him, he could not bring himself to look down, instead he stared fixedly at the winch hook that was directly in front of him. All of a sudden he found himself dangling in space and slowly spinning round, one moment he saw the winch man in the door way and the next moment nothing but gray space, the winch man disappeared and he realised he was being lowered down. It was one of the most unnerving experiences he ever had to suffer in his life.

Being unable to look down Charles could not see where he was going and on what he was going to land and at that moment of time he could not care less as he hung on for dear life to the winch wire. Charles was surprised when he saw Bridge windows of a ship in front of him and immediately felt somebody taking hold of his ankles and gently guiding him on to the deck. He was quickly unclipped from his harness and hurriedly taken to the after end of the ship where the accommodation block was situated. He was shown into the dining saloon which was quite crowded.

"Where the hell am I?" he asked no one in particular.

"You are on board the BP Tanker m.v. 'British Tay'" someone answered "We have been part of the Task Force almost from the outset of the emergency. We served as an oil storage vessel as the Task force sailed southwards for the Falklands, now we are empty and as soon as we get all you guys aboard we will head northwards to Ascension Island."

B. P. Tanker M. V. 'British Tay' 25,000 GR Ton.

"Now that's the best bit of news I have heard in days" a delighted Charles said, and he removed his survival suit and life jacket.

"I hope I never have to wear those bloody things ever again" he said with some feeling.

Charles glanced around the room and he recognised quite a few faces from the 'Conveyor' who had not been on 'HMS Alacrity'; they had been picked up by other ships in the Task Force. Their rafts had become separated from the main body of rafts and it was a while before they had been found and rescued. He picked out Keith, the fourth engineer, and went across to him. "What in hell were you trying to tell me in the 'chopper' I couldn't make it out at all with all that noise?" he asked.

"I was trying to tell you that the co-pilot you were sitting behind was none other than Prince Andrew."

"Was it?" an astounded Charles replied "Well!!! I suppose we can all say that we were given a Royal lift off!" they laughed out aloud.

Charles continued to circulate amongst the survivors and listened to their stories how they got off the 'Conveyor' and how they were rescued.

He came across a group that was talking animatedly and he recognised some of them were in the forward fire party on the 'Conveyor'.

"How did you guys get off the 'Conveyor'?"

"That is some story Charles I can tell you" John Brocklehurst the Chief Officer replied.

"We had been cut off from the rest of the ship by the inferno and from any life rafts, and were stranded on the fore deck. We owe our lives to two people, a guy called Nick Martin, a Chief Petty Officer in the Navy, he acted as a flight deck officer who stood amongst all the dense smoke and the flames coming out from the vents on deck to guide down an equally brave helicopter Pilot to land on the foredeck twice and lift us off.

"If those two very brave and courageous Navy lads had not been there to rescue us I would not be talking to you here today, that's for sure."

"Where did they take you?"

"We were taken to the aircraft carrier "Invincible" and treated like hero's before being transferred to here."

"You won't be knocking the Navy in future after all they have done for you, will you?"

"I certainly will not, you can bet your life on that" the Chief Officer adamantly replied.

A number of Naval Petty Officers who had been amongst the twelve people who had been crammed into a cabin next door to Charles's cabin on the 'Conveyor' had been on board the 'British Tay' from the previous evening and knowing that sleeping accommodation was going to be at a premium had set about liaising with the Officers and crew to arrange for them to double up in their cabins. They did a sterling job, Charles was allocated one of the third engineer's cabins along with Brian Williams which had an adjustable bunk for either double or single use. Charles eyed the bunk situation with some apprehension.

"If you think I am going to sleep with you Brian in that bunk you better have another think" Charles firmly stated.

"It's all right Charles, I am quite happy to kip on the settee."

"Thank God for that."

Before they could start arranging things in the cabin there was a knock on the door.

"Come in if you have a crate of ale" Charles cheerfully shouted.

The door slowly opened and there stood Petty Officer Dawes looking very apprehensive about the invitation to come in, he had also been allocated to share their cabin.

"Well I'll be damned" exclaimed Charles " Look who's here, if it isn't the bearded wonder himself who held on to the rafts with me to keep us together, are you sharing with us as well?"

"Yes I am" he quietly replied "but I haven't got any ale."

"Never mind that, come on in and welcome to our sumptuous boudoir" laughed Charles, sweeping his arms around the room.

"Thank you."

"Let me introduce you to Brian Williams, third engineer on the late 'Atlantic Conveyor', we have just been sorting out our sleeping arrangements, now you are here we will have to do it all over again."

"I am sorry to be such a bother" he said and shook hands with Brian.

"No problem rearranging the sleeping places, luckily the mattresses are two single ones, push the bunk into a single size and chuck one mattress on the deck and I will kip on that, the Petty Officer can then sleep on the settee, simple isn't it?" concluded Brian.

Charles was not going to argue about those arrangements, he had the bunk and that was all he wanted. "You don't snore do you Dawesy?" quizzed Charles.

"I don't think I do I have never heard myself snore" he said with a smile.

"Good, then you can stay in this cabin". There was just enough room for the three of them to be comfortable, they had their own bathroom and toilet and it was to be their home for the next eight days or so until they reached Ascension Island.

After arranging their cabin to their liking, for the second time, there was another knock on the door.

"Who the hell is it now?" cursed Charles. "You would think our cabin was a whore house in New Orleans."

"It's only me" said a voice and in walked Graham, the second engineer.

"What the hell do you want, we have no ale in here, yet" Charles heavily emphasised the 'yet'.

"Is there any room in here for me? The cabin allocated to me is far too cramped I have not been able to find a space in it to even lie down."

"What makes you think there is room in here?" Charles wanted to know.

"Now hold on Charles" interrupted Brian. "If I remember rightly from a similar ship I once sailed on we can unbolt the settee from the bulkhead, then we will be able to jam it into the corner between the bottom of the bunk and the bulkhead, this should give us enough room at the other end of where the settee was for Graham to put up his camp bed."

"Sounds practical, let's give it a try and see if your master plan works" said a sceptical Charles.

When all the moving about had finished everything fitted just as Brian had predicted. "How's that then Charles?" a rather pleased Brian said.

"Great for sleeping, but there is absolutely no bloody space at all for walking about" moaned Charles.

"Why not fold up the camp bed, take the mattress off the deck and shove it on the bunk during the daytime, there should be enough room to move about then" suggested the young Petty Officer.

"Good idea, you Navy chaps have got some brains after all" Graham laughingly commented.

"To be serious for a moment Graham, have you seen Jim Stewart our Chief?", a worried Charles asked.

"No I haven't but he must be somewhere around, why?"

" As you know he was held back from leaving the 'Alacrity' to join a team to be sent to the 'Conveyor' to see if anything was salvageable from her. Do you know or have you heard if he got back safely?"

"I can put your mind at rest about that right away, they never went, the whole plan was abandoned when the news came through that she had sunk" interjected the Petty Officer.

"Thank God for that" a much relieved Charles said " it was a damn stupid idea in the first place and I told him so."

"I totally agree with you, but that's when the Navy prove they have no brains at all" Graham said smiling across at the Petty Officer "present company excluded of course."

"Well what's done is done let's get back to the present" said Brian.

"Hold on a minute" said Graham "I noticed you were wincing as if in pain from time to time as we were moving these things about, is your shoulder still bothering you Charles?"

"It does from time to time, but nothing I can't cope with these days I just have to get on with it, it is improving as the days go by."

"OK, now all the medical reports are in, let's get down to the nitty gritty of our situation here" interrupted an unsympathetic Brian. "What's most important is to take stock of our few meagre belongings, our clothing is adequate, but what about the rest of our gear like soap, toothpaste, razors etc.etc.. First off we will put everything we have got on Charles's bunk then we will be able to see how we stand" Brian suggested.

All four of them placed what few toiletries they had on Charles's bunk and it made a pitiful pile consisting of one toothbrush, half a tube of tooth paste, a comb, two packets of disposal razors and a can of shaving cream.

"Is that all we have?" exclaimed Brian.

"Yep, that's the bloody lot, to quote a well known saying 'all our worldly possessions' Charles replied.

"We can't add to it either as there is no NAFFI on board here like on the 'Alacrity' added the Petty Officer.

"The crew are short of these necessities as well, being out here for so long so they won't be able to help us, the best way is to pool everything" Brian suggested.

"It's the only way" replied Charles "the worst part of it we have only got one toothbrush between the four of us and it's not very pleasant sharing such a personal item as a toothbrush, is it?"

"But we can't do anything else Charles, there is no other way we can clean our teeth" said Graham " I've got a mouth on me like the bottom of a parrot's cage already."

Charles shuddered at the thought of sharing a toothbrush with anyone let alone Graham in his dental situation. "Right then, let's have a few rules and regulations shall we? We have about eight days before we reach Ascension, so we will draw up a rota as to who is the first to use our precious toothbrush first on each morning and after we have used it, it must be thoroughly cleaned and rinsed by each individual and we will only clean our teeth in the morning, no more than that" Charles strongly stipulated.

"You are one fussy bugger, aren't you Charles?" said Brian grinning. "but that is the fairest and most hygienic way of sharing in these circumstances.

With all the sleeping and toiletries problems more or less resolved they all settled down into a semblance of a routine as the 'British Tay', at full speed, headed North away from the war zone and the Task force. As they steamed steadily along Charles found the days boring, he passed some of the time away by making himself a sort of kitbag out of discarded mail bags so that at least he would have something to carry any accumulated belongings in that he might acquire on his way home. The Navy personnel on board also kept them busy by requesting that the survivors from the 'Atlantic Conveyor' write a short summary of what happened to them between the time the 'Conveyor' was hit and their rescue by whichever ship they had got to, to see if they were helpful in finding out about some of the missing crew.

Although these reports did help in passing away more time during the first few days on board the 'British Tay' Charles found it difficult and distressing recalling all that had happened to him during that dramatic time.

"How are you getting along with your report Graham?" asked Charles

"Not bad, but listen I read one of the Navy mechanic's report, he had a pretty hair raising time. He had only been transferred over to us the day before, apparently he was working on the repair of a helicopter in the improvised workshop on B Deck when he felt the bang as the Exocet hit the ship. He turned around and saw a huge ball of fire racing towards him and he dropped everything and ran for his life up the ladder to A Deck. There he became completely disorientated, having just joined the ship, he didn't know where he was, but by good luck he did manage to find his way to the after deck and seeing the fire raging there, without a moments hesitation, thinking all was lost, he just jumped over the stern into the sea.

He fortunately had his lifejacket with him but did not put it on in his rush to get off the blazing ship. He managed to struggle into it whilst treading water, but he swallowed a lot of sea water during his efforts to get into it and he was violently sick. Luck was still with him because a helicopter Pilot spotted him in the water almost immediately and rescued him".

"The Gods were certainly looking after him all right" said Charles.

Alcohol was rationed simply because of the extra people aboard. Everyone was allowed six cans of beer or the equivalent in spirits. Charles had quickly come to an arrangement with Graham, as soon as he heard about the allocation of alcohol; he could have his beer ration and he would have Graham's spirit ration, Charles loved his Gin and Tonics. Bar hours were before lunch, before dinner and a few hours in the evening. As the days passed everyone became noticeably more relaxed and time did not seem to hang so heavily on their hands.

In order to alleviate the boredom further, Jim Stewart volunteered his surviving staff to assist the engineers on the 'British Tay' with deck repairs. This took a couple of days, eased the workload on the ship's staff and made the time pass more quickly on the passage up to Ascension Island. The surviving catering staff also assisted the chef on the tanker, as obviously a lot more meals were required with the large crew on board.

One evening they decided to have a party, Charles noticed a bottle of sherry on a shelf behind the bar and asked for one having convinced the young barman that sherry was not classed as alcohol but as a non-fortified wine. He got one and so did all the rest of the party. It was a very pleasurable evening and culminated in high spirits at the end of the party when one of the ships officers offered ten pounds to anyone who would throw the Captain, who was in his full uniform, into the swimming pool, this was accomplished amid loud cheers. The Captain took it all in good spirits and did not resent his dunking, but no more bottles of sherry appeared in the bar.

At last, on the evening of June 5th Charles stood on deck and watched the 'British Tay' go to an anchorage at the Ascension Island. Soon afterwards a helicopter came out with all their mail and the news they were to disembark the following morning by launch. Charles packed his few bits and pieces into his home made kitbag and decided to have an early night.

"Its going to be a long and tiring journey home" he said to himself.

18

ON ASCENSION ISLAND

Charles woke the next morning after a surprisingly good night's undisturbed sleep, considering the cramped conditions in the cabin. He did not get up immediately - he was third in line for the use of the communal toothbrush - he just lay there savouring the thoughts of going home and seeing Betty again. The young Petty Officer, who had first call on the toothbrush that morning, had gone out of the cabin as soon as he had finished his spell in the bathroom to give the others more room in which to move about, this was the routine they had adopted. Charles had just finished his allotted chores in clearing up the cabin for daytime use when he returned.

"Guess what you guys?" he announced.

"What now?" they all chorused back.

"Change of plans again, last night we were told we would be taken off by launch but a heavy swell has got up and the launches will not be able to get alongside us so it's back to the good old helicopter ride again."

"If I am ever asked to take a ride in a helicopter again, after this lot, I will shoot the sods who offer it to me" declared Charles. They all smiled at Charles's pronouncement knowing his fears of heights.

At 0900hrs they were assembled on deck in pairs, Charles was coupled with

Brian, as they awaited the arrival of the helicopters. Brian turned to Charles and said mischievously "You know we will have to stop meeting like this."

"Yes I know my wife will be furious if she ever finds out" they both laughed aloud.

In no time at all they were winched up and landed on an airstrip on the Island and driven by bus to an open air cinema being used as a reception area. It was the first time Charles had been on dry land since leaving Devonport on April 25th. Uniforms of the different services were all laid out in the reception area, but Charles noticed nothing of the Merchant Navy variety.

"That's typical of them, we are forgotten about already, things never bloody change, we are soon forgotten when its all over, par for the course I suppose, we shouldn't think otherwise" Charles said to himself.

One thing that Charles had noticed was the change in the weather, it was like a mid-summers day, the sun was shining out of a clear blue sky and the temperature was soaring into the eighties and getting hotter by the hour. They were invited to help themselves to any clothing they may find useful, or any other articles they felt they needed.

"The first thing I am grabbing is a couple of sets of underwear, I can hardly wait to get out of these sand paper "Y" fronts the Navy issued us" said Charles.

"I see they have been supplied by courtesy of Marks and Spencers" replied Brian.

"I don't care if they are supplied by the inmates of Walton Gaol, Brian, anything's got to be better than what I have on now and then my next priority is a toothbrush, God, will I be glad to have my own toothbrush" Charles fervently said.

"They're my priorities as well Charles, let's go and get them before they all disappear."

Charles picked out various items of clothing, bearing in mind the weather in Ascension and the weather when they get home to England, he also chose a

Naval Officers holdall to carry all his purchases. In typical Naval procedure Charles had to sign for every article he had selected.

"Is this so you can charge me at a later date?" he asked.

"I doubt it sir, it's just so we can bill the MoD for what has been used" a Naval attendant replied.

Two representatives from Cunard entered the reception area, Charles recognised Mr.Butler from personnel but did not know who the other person was. Mr.Butler called for the attention of all the 'Atlantic Conveyor' crew and commenced to speak.

"I would like to introduce you to Captain Holdrup of our Operations Department, we have been sent here by Cunard to make sure all your needs are catered for and all the arrangements for getting you home as soon as possible. Firstly, I have been given the authority by Cunard to issue you all with a 'sub' against the wages you have accumulated."

"How bloody generous of them, why couldn't they give us a 'sub' for nothing? the Navy did" a querulous voice interrupted.

"I was given no authority to do such a thing, may I continue?" He paused for a moment "Right ho! then I shall carry on, your flight home will be leaving Ascension Island at 0100hrs tomorrow morning, you will be on board an RAF VC 10, it has none of the refinements of a BOAC plane, but every effort is being made to make your journey home as comfortable as possible. Two WAAF Stewardesses will be in attendance to serve you your meals and to bring you coffee or tea whenever you require it. We have also arranged for up to date copies of all the national newspapers to be on board, this should help you pass some of the time away.

There will be one stop on the journey for re-fuelling at Dakar, West Africa. I have been informed that it should take about one hour to re-fuel but well knowing the unreliability of West African services this information could be a little optimistic. It promises to be a long haul home, never-the-less if all goes to plan you should arrive at Brize Norton exactly at twelve noon on June the 7th. Finally and I always keep the best news till the end, Cunard, at their own expense, I hasten to add, have arranged for your nearest and dearest members of your family to meet you as you land at Brize Norton. I think that covers everything. Are there any questions you would like to ask?"

"How do we get home from Brize Norton with all our family?" Charles asked.

"That will all be arranged, again courtesy of Cunard, when you arrive at Brize Norton Mr. Drought, nothing is being spared to get you home as quickly and as comfortably as possible. You will be delighted to know Mr.Drought, that your wife, two sisters and brother-in-law will be at Brize Norton to greet you"

"That is wonderful news Mr. Butler" an overjoyed Charles replied "Thank you very much"

"My pleasure" said a beaming Mr. Butler. "Now, I would like you all to listen very carefully to what Captain Holdrup has to say"

Captain Holdrup stood up. "Good morning gentlemen, I feel particularly privileged to speak to you after all you have been through but you may not realise this that you are all very much in the news at home and your arrival is naturally, very eagerly awaited by your loved ones but also every news hawk that the media can provide. What you do not know, most of you have already appeared by name and photograph in both National and Local newspapers.

I must emphasise to you all that there is still a war going on in the South Atlantic and you have seen what is going on down there at first hand therefore it is inevitable that some of you are going to be interviewed by the media. I must stress gentlemen that you must be most careful in what you say and confine your answers to accounts of your own personal survival. Do not mention the names of ships or aircraft or anything of that nature, some of these reporters will make a story out of an innocent phrase and completely change the whole context of it just for sensationalism especially those from the Sun, the Daily Mirror and the Star. I hope you understand the need to be discreet., but please do remember what I have just told you. I have nothing else to say to you other than I wish you all a safe and speedy onward journey home"

"Thank you Captain Holdrup for that information" said Mr. Butler " and now gentlemen, as you wait for take off time which is some way off, please feel free to avail yourselves of all the facilities and arrangements that have been made for you during your stay on the Island, but remember to be careful not to imbibe too much alcohol as the RAF pilots do not take too kindly to persons who have over indulged aboard their aircraft, disregarding the fact what you have been through, they can prevent you from boarding and thus prolong your arrival back home.

Are there any questions and are you all satisfied with what you have heard?" There was no response, Mr.Butler continued "You have a long flight ahead of you and I do not wish to keep you standing around too long but I would just like to reiterate what Captain Holdrup said in wishing you all a safe journey home and a long and peaceful future, you have all deserved it". There was a smattering of applause as Mr.Butler and Captain Holdrup left the hall. Charles, the Chief and Graham Ross drifted outside but it was too hot for them and they soon returned to the small bar. Charles was far from enthusiastic at the thought they would be sitting there all day waiting for their flight home.

"What the hell are we going to do to pass the time away, we can't sit here all day we will all be smashed by the time of our flight and you know what old Butler said 'get tanked up and you are at the back of the queue for going home' probably have to go by ship" groaned Charles.

Before anyone could answer Charles they were approached by a Welfare Officer, attached to the MoD "Good afternoon lads, you are all looking very glum what's your problem?"

"We are thinking about the long wait ahead of us before our flight and what we can do to make the time pass quickly, we can't sit here all day" Charles stated.

"Your problems are solved" the W.O. cheerfully replied "the locals have gone to great lengths to lay on their own little reception, they class it as a privilege and a pleasure to entertain you, please come with me and I will introduce you to them."

They quickly downed their drinks and followed the W.O. to the reception hall. A small group of people were standing in the hall as they entered, and elderly lady approached them "Good afternoon gentlemen, please do not think you are putting us to any trouble, let me introduce you to Mr. and Mrs. John Cave, John is our Island school teacher, and Mr. and Mrs. Sonny Newman, Sonny works for Cable and Wireless, they will be your hosts during your short stay with us."

After all the introductions and formal exchanges of names had been made, they were taken to their hosts' lovely homes given drinks and then went with their hosts on a comprehensive tour of the whole island. Charles was completed fascinated with the tour of the island from Turtle Beach where every year the turtles came struggling up above the water line to lay their eggs to Green Mountain where there is lush vegetation and the small farms' green fields with sheep and cattle grazing on them. The peacefulness and tranquillity of these pastoral scenes profoundly affected Charles and it made a very pleasant and entertaining day for them all and time passed swiftly by.

At dinner that evening when making their farewells, Charles said "Friends, I am speaking for us all when I say what kindly people and gracious hosts you have been to give up your time to help us through a potentially boring day. It has been an unforgettable experience, we will never forget you and all you have done for us, God bless you".

They were driven back to the reception hall, exchanged addresses, and made their last somewhat emotional farewells. They stood and watched them drive away until they were out of sight, Charles turned to the Chief and Graham. "It's good to know there are still a lot of wonderful people in this world of ours".

19

HOMEWARD BOUND

Around about midnight Charles boarded one of the convoy of RAF lorries to take them to the airstrip were a VC 10 was waiting to airlift them home. "Not much comfort in these bloody seats" he said as he sat down "reminds me of an old Liverpool tram seat" he grumbled happily.

"Hey! Charles I would travel all the way in a wheelbarrow with a square wheel just to get home" came a laughing reply.

The lorries bumped and swayed their way through the darkness and on to the airstrip and they boarded the plane immediately. As Charles sat down he became aware there was something very different about the interior of the plane, then it suddenly dawned on him, all the seats were facing rearwards instead of forwards as in civilian aircraft.

"Excuse me Miss" he called out to one of the WAAF stewardesses.

"Yes sir."

"Why are all the seats back to front? It's very unusual isn't it?"

"No sir, all the RAF passenger aircraft are fitted out this way, in their study of air crashes their researchers are convinced that passengers have a better chance of survival if they are facing to the rear of the plane."

"Oh! I thought it was because we wouldn't be able to see what we were going to crash into" Charles said with a smile.

When everyone was seated the pilot welcomed them all on board and apologised for the lack of leg room explaining that the powers that be had decided to double up on the numbers on board but everything would be fine.

The first few hours passed quite quickly for Charles, he had a light supper, a couple of cups of coffee and read a few British newspapers, eventually he fell asleep and awoke as they made their descent into Dakar airport.

The aircraft Public Address system came on "This is your pilot speaking, we will be landing in seven minutes at Dakar, the refuelling will take no longer than an hour but due to some international ruling you are not allowed to use the available facilities in the transit lounge of the airport, you will be allowed to leave the plane to exercise your legs by walking up and down the tarmac near to where we will be refueling."

"How bloody considerate of them" thought Charles sarcastically "and I am bursting for a leak."

Charles climbed out of the plane and wandered away from the crowd and in the darkness he made out the shape of a deep monsoon ditch at the end of the tarmac and proceeded to raise the level of the water in the ditch, just then a voice said "Great minds think alike," it really startled him he nearly lost his grip on his 'hose pipe'.

"Who the hell's that?" he exclaimed.

"Captain Layard, and I needed to 'point percy at the porcelain' just as much as you did" he replied in the good old Australian parlance.

They had a little chat whilst they enjoyed themselves and finishing with the usual flourish walked back together, this did help the circulation quite a bit after the cramped conditions on board the plane. Charles re-boarded the plane for the final leg of his journey home, he was beginning to get the first onset of the 'channels'.

To the surprise of everyone the refueling did take only one hour, a record for

West Africa for being on time. Charles fell asleep again soon after take off from Dakar, he was relieved to leave the place as much as he was when leaving Freetown, those many weeks ago. He had an inbuilt prejudice for all West African ports but this was shared by many seafarers from all over the world.

Charles was awakened by the pilot announcing over the public address system that they were now above the English Channel and flying eastwards along the South Coast. He looked out of his small side window, it was a glorious clear summers day and to Charles dear England never looked more beautiful from his vantage point. He actually felt he was going to cry, it was such a welcome sight, a sight more than once during the past weeks he thought he would never see again. The plane made its descent and landed and stopped altogether, the plane remained stationary for some time and then proceeded to taxi ever so slowly towards the terminal buildings at Brize Norton.

Everyone on board were eager to get off the plane, no more so than Charles, the thought of seeing Betty again and holding her in his arms set his heart beat racing uncontrollably.

"What's the hold up, are we going to do a lap of honour around the airfield before we get off this bloody plane?" someone shouted out. They all laughed at this remark, they were all 'straining at the bit' to disembark and rush to their loved ones.

"Please remain seated with your seat belts fastened until the plane has come to a halt" the pilot ordered over the Public Address system. Charles peered out of his window and was absolutely amazed to see what appeared to him as hundreds of people waving flags and cheering.

"I didn't expect to see such a reception as this, it's going to be pretty embarrassing walking through that lot" he thought to himself, At last the plane came to a gentle halt and the doors were opened, again orders came over the Public Address system "We will be disembarking by sections please remain seated until your section is called to disembark".

The RAF personnel left the plane first, then the magic moment for Charles came, the one he had been waiting for, for what seemed an eternity. "Will all

<u>*Welcome Home*</u>

R. A. F. Brize Norton - June 7th 1982
Lord Matthews (white coat) Cunard chairman
shaking hands with Charles Drought

The real welcome home for Charles Drought by his family.
L-R John (Brother-in-law), Betty, Charles, Diana and Rose (Sisters)

the survivors from the 'Atlantic Conveyor' please make your way to the exit door and disembark" the Public Address system announced.

Strangely there was no concerted rush for the doorway, in a quiet and orderly way they made their way to the exit point. Charles reached the doorway at the top of the steps and was rather awed at the sight of the welcoming committee all waiting to greet them, they stood in a crescent shape at the bottom of the aircraft steps. Amongst the welcoming dignitaries Charles recognised Lord Matthews, Cunard's Chairman, representatives from Cunard Personnel and representatives from the Merchant Navy Officers and Seamens Union. As he walked down the aircraft steps, following the others, he could hear sustained cheers and applause from the crowd as each individual appeared in the doorway of the plane at the top of the steps and started to descend to the tarmac.

Charles reached the bottom of the steps and was duly welcomed home by the reception committee, shaking hands with them all.

"Please come with me sir" said a young RAF Officer, and he was led towards the airport buildings. Charles followed the Officer along the tarmac anxiously scanning the crowd for any sign of Betty or his family, everyone he passed seemed to want to shake his hand and slap him on his back, he also noticed television cameras recording his passage across the tarmac.

He was shown inside to a large brightly lit building decorated with flags and streamers, it was absolutely packed with people and the noise was deafening. People were laughing, crying, talking and shouting, little children were screeching with joy as they were hoisted high above their overjoyed returning fathers' heads. Charles looked around the milling crowd quite bewildered and then suddenly Betty was there and their eyes met, it was such an emotional moment for them both. Charles had to fight hard not to shed a tear, they just stood there gazing at each other savoring every minute of this most precious moment, almost in disbelief that at last he was safely home. The noise from the crowd seemed to cease and the people seemed to disappear, Charles could only see his beloved Betty and as if by some magic signal they both started to walk towards each other.

To Charles it seemed to be the longest walk in his life, they met and he took her gently into his arms and kissed her longingly and tenderly, he could feel her trembling with emotion.

"It's wonderful to see you again darling, there have been moments when I did not think I would ever see you or hold you again".

Betty held Charles at arms length and looking at him through moist filled eyes said "I told you I would pray for you every day and ask God to keep you safe, and I did and he has answered my prayers, and I told you, you will be all right and you'll make it, remember?"

"How could I forget it Betty" Charles smiled back at her.

At that very moment a shaft of sunlight streamed through a small window high above them and shone directly behind Betty through her hair giving her that ethereal appearance he had seen on their last night together before he sailed to the Falklands and when it appeared to him as he struggled up the safety net to be rescued by the HMS 'Alacrity'. Charles was quite taken aback but decided that this was not the time nor the place to mention such a remarkable re-occurrence, he would choose a more quiet and intimate moment to tell Betty at some later date.

Charles's two sisters and brother-in-law had stood at a respectable distance away to allow Charles and Betty to have their precious moment of reunion alone. After a while Charles waved to them and beckoned them over and he was swamped with hugs, kisses, tears of joy and questions from everyone, he found it all very confusing but he enjoyed every minute of it. During this reunion with all his family a young man approached Charles.

"Excuse me, would you mind if I did a short interview with you?" he asked. "Who are you?" Charles sharply replied, mindful of the speech Captain Holdrup had given to them prior to leaving Ascension.

Granda T. V. News

"I do apologise, I should have introduced myself first, I am Richard Madeley, a presenter from Granada Television."

"I see, but I cannot answer any questions regarding the ship's whereabouts or any other ships or anything of that sort of nature, I will only answer questions about my experiences aboard the 'Atlantic Conveyor' when she was hit by an Exocet and how I got away from her" Charles stated firmly, still very wary of any interviewers.

"That's fine with me, no problem at all, could we all move away from the main concourse and take the interview in a less noisy atmosphere?"

"Certainly" a more assured Charles replied.

B. B. C. News

The interview went well but Charles felt very nervous throughout and held on tightly to Betty's hand. Richard Madeley true to his word did not at any time ask any questions that Charles would have declined to answer. The interview had just finished when a young woman came rushing up to Charles and breathlessly asked " I am Joan Thirkettle from ITN's News at Ten, would you give a short interview for the news going out tonight?" Charles could hardly refuse having already given an interview for Granada.

"Yes I will, but I must warn you I will not answer any questions regarding ships, aircraft or whatever concerning the situation down in the Falklands, just keep your questions relating to my experiences."

"Righto!, lets start to roll" was her very professional reply.

After a few preliminary questions about his experiences in the Falklands and his feelings on returning home she suddenly asked.

"Do you know anything of the whereabouts of Captain North who is listed as missing and what was he like to sail with?"

Charles was incensed at this question "Madam I

The welcoming crowds

consider those questions completely inappropriate and totally insensitive. I do not think it is right or proper to be asked in public to comment on his whereabouts or his ability as a ship's Master. I do not wish to answer any further questions or make any further comments, this interview is over, I bid you a good afternoon" Charles turned and walked away leaving a somewhat stunned Ms. Thirkettle and ITN film crew.

Charles and his family were ushered to a car and driven to an airfield near Brize Norton where a small plane was waiting to take them to Manchester. Betty who was at the best of times very reluctant to fly in any plane at all viewed this little aircraft with some trepidation.

"How are we all going to fit into that plane with the television crew and all their paraphernalia?

The sheer joy of the reunion
C. P. O. (R. N.) Nick Martin and family.

"They will have arranged everything Betty."

"More importantly will we be able to take off with that load on board?" a very worried Betty wanted to know.

"Stop worrying love, they will have worked everything out there will be no problems, honestly" said Charles, trying to soothe her nervousness.

"I hope so" a not totally convinced Betty replied.

Charles walked up to the pilot who was supervising the loading of all the equipment. "I say is there any room for my gear in there?"

"What have you got and how heavy are they?"

"Just the two bags, one a holdall courtesy of the Royal Navy and one Do-it-Yourself mail-cum-kit-bag with hardly anything in either of them, all my gear is somewhere at the bottom of the South Atlantic".

"That's fine, I will pack them in the luggage compartments in each wing, now get on board and let's take off."

Despite all Betty's premonitions for the inability to take off, it and the flight to Manchester went perfectly. Although Charles was very tired he enjoyed the flight tremendously especially when he was invited to open a locker alongside his seat and help himself to a beer or whatever he wanted. They landed at Manchester Airport and were quickly ushered through customs, said their farewells to the Television crew, climbed into a car and were driven home.

Charles arrived at his home and was amazed at what he saw, the house had been decorated by the whole neighbourhood and friends from far and near with bunting, union flags, red ensigns, streamers and red, white and blue paper roses covered all the bushes in the front garden. To complete the transformation of his house a huge banner proclaiming "WELCOME HOME" hung from the upstairs windows. They were all there to greet him and cheer him home.

"I didn't know so many people had heard of me or I was missed by so many people" an overwhelmed Charles said to Betty.

"You are their hero Charles, and they all want to show their feelings for what you have been through and come home safely" a very proud Betty replied.

As he made his way from the car to his front door they cheered him, shook his hand, slapped him on his back, and shouted 'Welcome home', 'great to see you back' and other messages of welcome, some of the ladies even kissed him. When Charles reached the open front door Betty softly said to him "It would be nice if you thanked them, they would appreciate that."

"I was just going to ask you should I say anything to them."

Charles turned around "Well folks I never expected such a reception when I got home, it has come as a complete surprise but I would like to thank you all very sincerely for coming here today to welcome me back and also to thank you all for the wonderful way you have given support to Betty while I have been away, you must be the best friends and neighbours in the world. I would like to ask you all in to a party, but you will appreciate I am very, very tired. I have been travelling for over fourteen hours but rest assured there will be a 'do' at some later date and you will all be invited. Thanks again for all you have done, God Bless you all."

They cheered him to the roof tops as he went into his house and closed the door on the outside world.

The rest of the afternoon passed by in a sort of daze, the telephone never stopped ringing as he read the many welcome home cards, he even had two telegrams sent to him from folk he had not seen or heard from for years. In the evening when his family had all gone, he sat down with Betty and watched the television programmes of their interviews at Brize Norton.

"I think they put our interviews together quite well don't you Betty?".

"Yes I do, but I felt strange looking at ourselves on television."

"It was kind of odd I agree but I am relieved and I am sure you are they did not try and make us look like and sound like village idiots."

"That's true Charles we did look and sound quite intelligent" they both smiled at each other.

"You get off to bed Betty I won't be too long following you, I just want to sit alone for awhile."

Betty instinctively knew Charles needed this moment to be alone, he often did this when he wanted to sort out the many thoughts that were racing through his mind.

Betty leaned across and kissed him gently on the cheek, a kiss that contained all the love in the world for her Charles, she had never been so happy in her life to have him safe and sound at home.

When Betty had left the room Charles stood up and went to the drinks cabinet and poured himself a large whisky and returned to sit in his favourite chair, he sighed deeply and took a long drink out of the glass. Deep in thought in the silence of the room, Charles relived nearly all that had happened to him from the time he left Liverpool until his return home.

"I never ever want to go through that again" he said to himself. " it was bad enough losing the ship, but how sad she took with her those men who had not had a chance to abandon her" he shook his head in remembrance of it all. With another deep sigh he finished off his drink, stood up and walked out of the darkened room.

"Thank you God, that you chose me to be one of the lucky ones to come home" were Charles's last thoughts as he made his way to bed.

20

THE FINAL HOURS OF
THE 'ATLANTIC CONVEYOR'

The account of the final hours of the 'Atlantic Conveyor' after the crew were forced to abandon her is taken from the log of the requisitioned deep sea tug 'Irishman'.

The tug 'Irishman' reached the 'Conveyor' on May 27th. This was the second day after the Exocet missiles had struck her the mortal blow. She was drifting at about two knots in a ten to twelve foot swell. Her possible recovery was considered vital because she was carrying much needed equipment. She was full of ammunition and fuel and in a very dangerous condition.

The 'Irishman's' bridge log reads as follows:

The bow section of the 'Conveyor' has been completely blown off either by internal explosions or rockets, probably both. All the accommodation sections were badly burnt. Some of the containers on the fore deck seemed to be intact. There is a burnt out helicopter on the after deck.

A large hole, approximately two feet in diameter was sighted. The hole, which is right through the ship's side plating, is on the Port side and below the accommodation but above the water line. The vessel is listing 15-18 degrees to starboard and is very noticeably down by the stern.

Most of the paint work has been burnt off, indicating very severe heat especially around the Engine Room area and the after end. Smoke is still escaping from forward and a smaller amount from the stern. After standing off for four hours it was adjudged safe enough for men to be put on board the smouldering hulk. Thirty minutes later they were reinforced by others in order to connect a tow line. The intention being to tow the 'Conveyor' away from the total exclusion zone which had been set up by the British Forces around the Falkland Islands. The tow line was connected and the tug proceeded, after having taken the tow connecting party off.

At about 0045hrs on the 28th May we experienced heavy strain on the towing gear, before any action could be taken the tow parted. Visibility was reduced by fog at that time to only 400 yards, the radar was adjusted to low range, one and a half miles, but only a small signal was picked up.

Against all regulations the searchlight was utilised and the target which had been recorded on the radar screen was identified as three large containers floating on the surface. After searching for an hour there was no sign of the 'Atlantic Conveyor' whatsoever. We could only assume that she had sunk and we left the area.

The 'Atlantic Conveyor' did not sink after the tow line broke but had drifted away into the fog and had been picked out on a radar screen by one of the assault ships in the area. The Naval Commanders conceived an ingenious plan to entice the Argentineans to use their last remaining Exocet on the hulk of the 'Atlantic Conveyor' and it worked perfectly. The ruling Junta in Buenos Aires claimed on May 28th that Super Etendards and Skyhawks had hit and seriously damaged the carrier HMS 'Invincible' on which the Queen's son Prince Andrew was serving. What the Argentineans had attacked was the useless hulk of the 'Atlantic Conveyor'. Naval carpenters had been put aboard her to change her outline with canvas and wood - rather like a film set - a flimsy but convincing superstructure until they had created a passable replica of the 'Invincible'.

It would not fool anyone close up, but with a few "protecting" destroyers around her to add authenticity, it could easily deceive a fast moving jet pilot. The Super Etendards dodged the fire from the "protecting" destroyer and the last precious Exocet the Argentineans had was released at the 'Conveyor' in their attack on what they thought was the 'Invincible'. She was struck amidships and was blown apart and quickly but quietly sank beneath the waves.

Although she failed in the attempt to deliver essential supplies to the land forces, in her death throes she did destroy the last remaining Exocet, the most feared and deadliest weapon in the Argentinean's armoury. That was her contribution to victory in the Falklands campaign.

The Tug 'Irishman' approaches the burnt out hulk of the 'Atlantic Conveyor' in an abortive attempt to salvage her.

21

THE 'ATLANTIC CONVEYOR; CREW LIST

Port of registry Liverpool, Official No. 337245. Net. tonnage. 7408.

Crew list April 14th 1982:

Ian Harry North	Master
John Keith Brocklehurst	Chief Officer
Philip Eric Bailey	2nd Officer
Martin Stenzel	3rd Officer
David Robert Egerton	Radio Officer
James Mailer Stewart	Chief Engineer
Graham Henry Ross	2nd Engineer
Charles John Drought	3rd Engineer (Senior)
Brian Robert Williams	3rd Engineer
Kieth Peter Adams	4th Engineer
Neil McGown	Chief Electrical Officer
Ian George Yorkston Jamieson	Purser
Boleslaw Czarnecki	Petty Officer 1 Engine Room Mech.
Frank Foulkes	Petty Officer 1 Engine Room Mech.
James Hughes	Petty Officer 2 Engine Room Mech.

Ernest Norman Vickers	Petty Officer 2 Engine Room Mech.
John Benjamin Dobson	Petty Officer 1 Deck.
George William Sutherland	General Purpose 1
John Dennis Irwin	General Purpose 1
John Joseph Garvey	General Purpose 1
John Harris	General Purpose 1
John Stuart Bartlett	General Purpose 1
Ross Lester Chambers	General Purpose 1
Gary Waynes Jenkins	General Purpose 1
Michael John Chapman	General Purpose 1
Edward Albert Jarvis	2nd Steward
William Sydney Tuck	Petty Officer 1 Cook
Ronald Garden	Petty Officer 1 Cook
John Henry Fletcher	2nd Cook
Harold Olsson	2nd Cook
Gary John Hutchins	Steward
Paul Nicholas Mileham	Steward

22

WAR BONUS PAYMENTS

When the 'Atlantic Conveyor' had passed below the 6° South line of latitude it was designated the vessel was in the war zone and immediately all crew members had their wages increased by 150% as a war bonus during the whole six weeks they spent in the war zone. The following figures are approximately what each rank would receive as a war bonus for six weeks.

Chief Officer	£2,496
Second Officer	£1,714
Third Officer	£1,418
Chief Engineer	£2,925
Second Engineer	£2,025
Senior Third Engineer	£1,845
Third Engineer	£1,714
Fourth Engineer	£1,519
Chief Electrician	£1,735
Radio Officer	£1,782
Purser	£1,634
Engine Mechanic	£1,314
G.P.1	£1,496
Second Steward	£1,225
Steward	£1,212
Chief Cook	£1,582
Second Cook	£1,184

23

THEY SHALL NOT GROW OLD
AS WE THAT ARE LEFT GROW OLD

We commit to the care and keeping of Almighty God, and honour the memory of those who gave their lives fighting in the South Atlantic on board the 'ATLANTIC CONVEYOR'.

The Cunard Personnel:

Captain Ian Harry North	Master	aged 55
John Benjamin Dobson	Bosun	aged 53
Frank Foulkes	E.R. Mech.	aged 48
James Hughes	E.R. Mech.	aged 50
Ernest Norman Vickers	E.R. Mech.	aged 58
David Reginald Hawkins	Steward	aged 28

The Royal Navy Personnel:

Adrian Onslow	Writer	aged 17
Edmund Flanagan	Writer	aged 23
Donald Pryce	Writer	aged.26

The Royal Fleet Auxiliary Personnel:

Ronald Hoole	Radio Officer	aged 24
NG Po	Laundry Man	aged 27
Chan Chi Sing	Laundry Man	aged 32

WE WILL REMEMBER THEM

24

WHERE ARE THEY NOW?

Mr. J. M. Stewart, Chief Engineer

Mr.Stewart returned to sea within two months of the sinking of the 'Atlantic Conveyor'. He was appointed by Cunard as Chief Engineer of the 'Atlantic Causeway'. He retired in 1988 and is living with his wife Mary in Broughty Ferry near Dundee. He is in good health and his favourite pastime is walking with his wife interspersed with gardening and D.I.Y. projects. He was Mentioned in Dispatches for his bravery on the 'Atlantic Conveyor'.

Mr. Graham Ross, 2nd Engineer

Mr.Ross returned to sea some three months after the sinking of the 'Atlantic Conveyor'. Cunard offered him a position as second engineer on the 'ACT 6'. He is a single man and living in Greasby on the Wirral. He is in good health and is still sailing as a Chief Engineer with P & O Nedlloyd.

Mr. Charles Drought, Senior 3rd Engineer
and his beloved wife Betty

Mr. Drought returned to sea within two months after the sinking of the 'Atlantic Conveyor'. Cunard offered him a position as senior third engineer on the 'Atlantic Causeway'. He served on other Cunard container vessels until 1995, when he had a gall bladder operation which eventually forced him to retire from the Merchant Service in July 1996, after having spent 37 years at sea.

On Easter Monday 1996 tragedy of the most disastrous news overtook Charles when his beloved wife was diagnosed as having breast cancer; it shattered their lives completely. In February 1997 his beloved Betty died

He is in good health and still speaks with pride that he was rescued by Prince Andrew and has the same birth date as him, February 19th. Still living in the same house he came home to from the Falklands he is an avid fan of jazz music and travels with friends to as many concerts they can get to. When asked if he could live his life again would he change anything after all he had been through his reply was typical of Charles "I would change one thing only to have Betty with me to share the evening of our lives together, I would not wish or want to change anything else".

Mr. B. Williams, 3rd Engineer.

Mr. Williams returned to sea three weeks after the sinking of the 'Atlantic Conveyor'. Cunard offered him a position as senior third engineer on the 'Atlantic Star' He held that position for twelve months when doctors diagnosed him as being severely diabetic in 1983 and declared him unfit to continue going to sea. He never worked again and lived with his parents in Bebington. He was awarded the Queens Gallantry Medal for his actions during the sinking of the 'Atlantic Conveyor'. He died in 1998 due to complications in his diabetic condition.

Mr. P. Bailey, 2nd Officer

Mr.Bailey returned to sea two weeks after the sinking of the 'Atlantic Conveyor'. Cunard offered him a position as second officer on the 'Atlantic Causeway'. He sailed for one voyage and was offered a position ashore with Cunard in Management Training. He is in good health and is head of his own Management Training company, On Track International Ltd, based in Hertfordshire. He is married with two children.

Mr. Boleslaw (Bill) Czarnecki, Engineer Mechanic

Mr. Czarnecki was Polish and because it was difficult to pronounce his surname let alone his first name he was always called 'Bill' by all who sailed with him. He had a very tough life, all his family were killed by the Germans or Russians, he alone escaped from imprisonment in 1943 and by various means made his way to England were he joined the RAF. After the war he was classed as a displaced person and he joined the Merchant Navy and served until his premature retirement in 1997.

During all that time he made many attempts to obtain British Citizenship but each time he was refused. It is nice to record that for the part he played on the 'Conveyor' he was at last granted British Citizenship. Everyone who sailed with him found him a pleasure to work with, a really likeable and helpful man and a true gentleman. He died of cancer in 2000.

Mr. E. A. Jarvis, 2nd Steward

Mr. Jarvis returned to sea two months after the sinking of the 'Atlantic Conveyor'. Cunard offered him a position as second steward on the 'Atlantic Causeway'. He retired from the sea in 1990 and went into catering ashore until he finally retired in 1998. He is in good health and married with two grown-up children. He has no serious hobbies but likes reading and gardening and visiting his three grandchildren.

25

EPILOGUE

For Charles Drought there are many emotional moments from his tour of duty in the South Atlantic during the Falklands campaign, moments that are indelibly stamped into his memory and they return from time to time in the form of 'flash backs' causing him sleepless nights. The nightmarish ordeal aboard the blazing 'Conveyor', his futile attempt to rescue the E. R. Mechanic who was pleading for help, he still hears the plaintiff cry of 'Help me, help me' in his dreams and awakens cold and shivering as if with a fever and his struggles in the life raft are never far from his thoughts. These recurring experiences have aged him beyond his years and changed his outlook on life immeasurably.

Everyone aboard the 'Atlantic Conveyor' on that fateful voyage upheld all the great traditions of the Merchant Service handed down from generation to generation. They were all civilians, they have always been so in the Merchant Service, but when the call came to help to defend the rights and freedom of other men and their countries they volunteered without a moment's hesitation. They felt it was their duty to do so, there was never any question in their minds. This was the tradition of the Merchant Service in all the past wars. In WW2 Admiral of The Fleet Lord Lewin wrote "The men of the Merchant Navy have set the seal for all time on my already strong admiration and respect for them. It is so much easier for us in our well-armed ships with high speed and manoeuvrability, to feel that we have a reasonable chance in the face of any determined and concentrated attacks, from the sea or the air. They on the other hand must feel like sitting ducks". The men of the Merchant Service on board the 'Conveyor', called to serve their country, did so with distinction once again. God forbid there should be any future wars, and these men of the Merchant Service would be called upon to serve their country again.

There are various memorials erected to commemorate those who made the supreme sacrifice fighting for the freedom of the Falkland Islands and cemeteries for them to rest in but there are no crosses, or stones, or inscriptions to mark the grave of the 'Atlantic Conveyor' and those who died with her. The cold grey unforgiving sea, the lowering dark clouds and the white capped waves blown high by the gales are all that marks their final resting place.

The Red Ensign flew proudly in that campaign, they did their duty to the full, may they now rest in peace. They have gained their immortality in the cause for the rights of their fellow men to live as they wished under the Union flag and in peace.

D. A. Clulow

26

ODE TO PEACE

Put peace into each others hands
And like a treasure hold it
Protect it like a candle flame
With tenderness enfold it.

Put peace into each others hands
Be gentle in our ways and sharing
Look people warmly in the eye
Our life is not for warring.

Put peace into each others hands
Take every means and measure
Make peace, give peace a chance
And share it like a treasure.

Put peace into each others hands
And let our warring lives cease
Drop the still dews of quietness
Forever in calmness and in peace.

AMEN.